BEETHOVEN

Complete Pianoforte Sonatas

Edited by

HAROLD CRAXTON

Annotated by

DONALD FRANCIS TOVEY

Volume I

THE ASSOCIATED BOARD OF
THE ROYAL SCHOOLS OF MUSIC

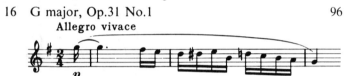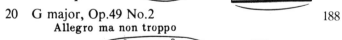

Volume III

PREFACE

A French musical scholar, Charles Bannelier, has said that an absolutely correct and authentic edition of Beethoven is *une chimère d'artiste, un rêve doré de critique*. But what do we mean by correctness and authenticity? How far do these qualities overlap? And are they not capable of such definitions as may make the pursuit of them more profitable than that of chimeras and rainbows?

A correct text of Beethoven is surely not as unattainable as a correct text of Shakespeare; with most of Beethoven's works we possess his final autographs and any number of sketches; and for some works we possess what is even more valuable, the proof-sheets of the first edition with his autograph corrections. In spite of these advantages, the conscientious editor finds innumerable problems of detail, not all of which can be definitely solved. We may doubt whether a complete list of the problems will ever be made even within the single category of the pianoforte sonatas. But Beethoven is by no means the most difficult composer to edit. He took the utmost pains to edit his own works; and if his utmost pains have still left many problems for us to solve, the difficulties lie deep in the nature of his style and are not to be removed by hasty conjecture. Beethoven is of all artists the one whom it is most impertinent to correct merely for the sake of system. His art is not tidy; but it is inexhaustibly thoughtful, and the editor who indulges in the habit of correcting Beethoven's discrepancies is depriving himself of innumerable opportunities of learning from Beethoven what would never have entered into his own editorial mind.

Apart from editorial interference, the main source of error in the text of Beethoven's works is the fact that Beethoven, though an excellent proof-reader, was not infallible. Most of his oversights concern accidentals. For these he had a better eye than Mozart, who seems, to judge by the facsimiles of his autographs now accessible to the public, to have deferred most of that question to the final proof-reading. But Mozart, though as subtle an artist as ever lived, is always systematic; and he could safely correct his proofs by rule of thumb, in this matter at all events. With Beethoven nothing is more unsafe than to correct him by aiming at uniformity. No musician is great enough to be justified in taking such a risk. What then constitutes that chimera, an absolutely authentic and correct edition of Beethoven? Evidently the 'correctness' must be Beethoven's. If it is merely the editor's, the authenticity has disappeared. We need not condemn a correction as being merely the editor's because that correction has not been made before. Circumstantial evidence may be tantamount to the best available knowledge of the workings of the artist's mind. It is almost the only evidence that classical scholarship has. Again, there are some points that occur systematically in manuscripts of certain periods. Beethoven, however, presents us with only one problem that can be classified under this heading, and then only because there is at the present day no consistent practice in the notation of phrase-markings and slurs. This topic will be dealt with below: it requires some light from the common-sense of other instruments than the pianoforte.

With artists like Beethoven and Shakespeare the editor must be both humble and intelligent. Beethoven presents no problems of authenticity. What was printed of his works in his lifetime was seen by him, and even the pirated editions encountered his denunciation. And in some ways he was astonishingly tolerant. There is an early English edition of the Op.106 Sonata in which the Scherzo is put after the Adagio, a disarrangement that fills us with consternation. But still more amazing is the fact that Beethoven, if he did not actually suggest this, consented to it on the ground that, as no English buyer would ever play the final fugue, it would be as well to end the sonata with a movement in the tonic! No sane editor would take this seriously as a variant reading; but we cannot on that account discredit the evidence of an edition published with Beethoven's consent.

From intimate knowledge of Beethoven's style a few simple editorial principles may safely be formulated.

Doubtful Readings

Where Beethoven could not make up his mind, the editor has no business to make it up for him. That is the player's business, since the player can play only one reading at a time. But the evidence of Beethoven's indecision must not be suppressed. Teachers who will not take the trouble to help their pupils in such matters had better themselves go to school again. Beethoven is not an artist who needs bowdlerising for family use. His sonatas are works of the same order (and sometimes on the same scale) as his string quartets and symphonies. It is not too much to say that the multiplication of editions that interpose a spoonfed conservatoire-tradition between Beethoven and the student has been a serious obstacle to the progress of musical culture for almost a century.

Intentional Irregularities

When Beethoven shows a discrepancy between parallel passages, as, for instance, between the exposition and the recapitulation of a movement in sonata form, the editor should never adjust it except where one of the readings is unintelligible in itself. Bülow, who combines the arbitrary exercise of his own preferences with the most violent diatribes against the vandalism of other editors, removes without comment a discrepancy in the first movement of the Sonata *Les Adieux*, Op.81a. The discrepancy may be admitted to be unconvincing though defensible; but whether we like it or not, the fact remains that it is not only in the autograph but actually written as a correction over the other reading! Beethoven's autographs, in the form in which he sent them to the publishers, may be untidy, but they seldom leave any doubt as to their meaning. They sprawl so widely over the page that there would be room for two alternative readings between most of the notes. And Beethoven is not fond of abbreviations. He cancelled two plates of the Op.97 Trio because he objected to an abbreviation which lay across the rhythm of some triplet quavers; and he insisted on printing out the long repeat of the Scherzo in full. Hence it is very risky to decide a reading on the guess that Beethoven has used an abbreviation which the printers have misunderstood.

Compass of the Pianoforte

The compass of the pianoforte hampered Beethoven in all his works for it. Up to the *Kreutzer* Sonata (Op.47) the compass was, as with Mozart, five octaves, from F to F. By the time the C minor Concerto (Op.36) was printed, the compass had been extended upwards to C, and Beethoven was able to improve the pianoforte part of that work accordingly. Later the compass varied, some instruments reaching the top F, some going down to the bottom C, and a few extending both ways. Beethoven's last sonatas show that he is not sure what will be available, for he sometimes restricts himself one way and sometimes the other. The finale of Op.101 is evidently for an instrument of wider compass than the other movements; and none of the three last sonatas, nor the Diabelli Variations and the Bagatelles, Op.126, have so wide a compass as Op.106. Beethoven sometimes thought of issuing a new edition of his earlier works revised so as to use the compass of later instruments. Perhaps it was a deeper instinct, as well as the pressure of new works, that prevented him from carrying out this project. It answered well enough with the C minor Concerto, where the changes were made while the composition was still his newest work. But Beethoven had little reason to trust his judgment as to how to treat his early works after his style had changed. To revise a work drastically down to the roots of its composition, as when the *Leonore* of 1805–6 became the *Fidelio* of 1814 – this was a noble task. But to alter the merely ornamental aspects of his earlier pianoforte style was a thing he would have done with hardly more sympathy than his pupil Czerny. We have, indeed, Czerny's own notes of some of the changes Beethoven made on the spur of the moment in playing his G major Concerto; and they are deplorable. Beethoven himself allowed only one of them to reach the printers.

Pianoforte Style

Beethoven writes for the pianoforte as for an instrument which he has thoroughly mastered. He could play his own pianoforte works: and this is a more important fact to be considered in the interpretation of them than any later developments of pianoforte technique. If the instrument has changed in the course of a century this is not going to make the interpretation of Beethoven easier. Much of the change would have been very welcome to him: for he was always writing for ideal instruments. But his ideals were very firmly rooted in facts; and the facts of Beethoven's pianoforte are not things we can safely neglect, nor are all modern developments in the direction of Beethoven's ideals. His deafness put it out of his power to correct his later works by experiment. But the results of this have been enormously exaggerated; and features of his style have been ascribed to deafness when they are not only the logical development of tendencies manifest in Haydn and Mozart but are also beautiful in themselves if sympathetic playing gives them a chance. This is particularly the case with the enormous distance Beethoven often allows between his treble and bass. From its earliest days one of the principal charms of the pianoforte was its suggestiveness. The earliest pianofortes were far less rich in tone than the best

harpsichords; yet composers and players cheerfully consented to lose all the octave-couplings and contrasts of colour that the several stops of a large double harpsichord provided. The direct control of touch by the player's fingers was worth more than any such material resources; and the fact that long notes on the pianoforte are evanescent was never felt as a hindrance to the suggestion of sustaining power.

In recent times the view has arisen that the character of the pianoforte results from the fact that its strings are struck by hammers; and from this the inference is drawn that a *cantabile* style is unnatural to the instrument, and that the chopstick technique of 'blind octaves' is the only true 'pianistic' style. This is the fallacy of confusing cause with effect. The essential character of the pianoforte is that of strings vibrating with an amplitude that steadily diminishes. The ear knows nothing as to the mechanical cause of this mode of vibration. But the ear is more sensitive to the diminution from *forte* to *mezzo-forte* than to that from *piano* to *pianissimo*. Now the 'half-period' of the vibrating string, *i.e.* the period within which the sound diminishes by half, is approximately constant. It follows from this that it is only in loud passages that the listener finds it difficult to believe that sustained pianoforte notes are lasting out their time. Again, the impression of a legato depends not nearly so much on the absence of gaps or overlaps between the notes as upon an even volume of tone. And when the notes are long enough to have diminished appreciably, the tones that must be matched are the ends of the notes rather than the beginnings. A fine *cantabile* on the pianoforte will always depend upon a sensitive ear and a readiness to adapt the touch to the minutest changes of circumstance both in the music itself and in the differences between one instrument and another.

Thus the mere possession of a good method of tone-production is not enough to produce even a plausible imitation of a legato. Many players exult in their capacity to bring the whole weight of their muscular apparatus on to every note. Their beautiful tone then reduces all melody to a series of bulges, and gives rise to the conviction that Mozart, Beethoven, and Brahms were all ridiculously mistaken in imagining that the pianoforte could combine with other instruments at all. As a matter of fact, only a very good string player can sustain a tone with a *diminuendo* anything like as gradual as that of a long note on the pianoforte. And the modern pianoforte is enormously superior in sustaining power to anything either Mozart or Beethoven ever knew. Yet the earliest pianoforte composers regarded the instrument as eminently a vehicle for *cantabile*; and Mozart is not afraid to make it play a sustained theme that has just been given out by the clarinet. And the violin and the clarinet have not increased in tone since Mozart's or even since Stradivarius's time. Clearly, then, the classical art of pianoforte playing was always an art of suggestion; and it makes no difference to the power of suggestion that the half-period of the pianoforte strings was far shorter a century ago than it is now.

Pedal

The thing that has become most changed by the longer tone of our instruments is the effect of the damper-pedal. This changed perceptibly during Beethoven's own lifetime; and his indications of pedalling must be studied with caution. Fortunately, like all composers who have a practical grasp of the conditions of good performance, Beethoven shows in this matter a common-sense which time does not invalidate. He indicates only the larger pedal effects which suit all conditions. It is not be supposed that he or any important composer (except Liszt in his very last works) attempts to indicate the use of the pedal for details of legato playing where harmonies are constantly changing. The art of playing without pedal at all is rarer than it ought to be. But it always was a special art and always will be so. We have plenty of testimony that Beethoven, while he was still able to hear what he was doing, used the pedal constantly, with the highest art and in ways that were not remotely indicated by his written directions. On the early pianofortes many things could be allowed which would sound very messy on our present instruments. Thus Beethoven could, in a *pianissimo*, take the whole first eight bars of the slow movement of the C minor Concerto with the pedal unchanged through all the modulations. In the first movement of the C♯ minor Sonata he probably never changed the pedal at all. Indeed, it seems as if the pedal did not act very readily, for in the slow movement of the C minor Concerto when Beethoven finds it necessary to specify changes for thick bass arpeggios he allows half a beat (at about 120 of the metronome – *i.e.* half a second) to make the change.

In the earliest days of the pianoforte it was even questionable whether dampers were worthwhile. Philipp Emanuel Bach said that an undamped instrument fired the imagination; thereby anticipating Schumann's morbid habit of extemporising with the pedal immovably down.

Be this as it may, Beethoven's pedal marks are full of interest and can, for the most part, be taken almost literally. Nobody, for instance, is justified in putting pedal into the arpeggios of the first theme of the finale of the C♯ minor Sonata. Beethoven explicitly reserves the pedal for the *sforzando* chords and sets great store by his staccato bass.

Again, what are we to say of the editor who before the *Prestissimo* of the finale of the *Waldstein* Sonata suppresses Beethoven's pedal-marks and retains the curious fact that Beethoven represents a bar's rest by two crotchet rests? Or an editor who retains the pedal-marks and simplifies the notation? The sole purpose of that notation is to show that Beethoven wishes the damper to fall on the second crotchet! In the G major Concerto he even fills out a $\frac{2}{4}$ bar with rests for two quavers and two semiquavers, in order to show that the damper falls on the last semiquaver rest. Again, in the Op.109 Sonata the position of the sign for change of pedal shows that the first movement is to be followed without break by the *Prestissimo*.

There is little or no difficulty in seeing where Beethoven's pedal-marks cannot be taken literally. Most of them concern big stretches of arpeggio with nothing to disturb them: but occasionally, as in the Rondo of the *Waldstein* Sonata, Beethoven indicates a pedal up a scale-passage which few teachers will venture to approve. But even here his pedal is quite possible for one bar if the initial bass octave is powerful and the scale taken lightly. No Chopin-player would hesitate to use a discreet pedal in a bass of similar purport in Chopin's F♯ minor Polonaise, where the notation in grace-notes shows the kind of scale needed. But we cannot nowadays continue Beethoven's pedal through his second bar where the scale descends again in staccato semiquavers. These demand full tone. On the other hand, a pianoforte that would tolerate pedal through the whole theme of the slow movement of the C minor Concerto cannot have sounded like a modern pianoforte without use of the pedal at all. In some ways it must have sounded more subtle than our most refined half-pedallings. Nothing less than our best efforts can replace the suggestiveness of the earlier pianofortes; and it is vexation of spirit to try and commit these efforts to musical notation. No two instruments require the same treatment. The player must train his ear and judge by it. One very interesting passage admits of a special treatment today. Beethoven was able to play the recitatives in the first movement of the D minor Sonata 'with open pedal' (as Haydn said in a sonata published in London in 1789). The effect was, as Beethoven desired, like a voice coming from a vault. Something very like it can be produced now by merely continuing to hold the low bass chord through the recitative; or, on large instruments, by the more cautious device of silently putting down that chord (or any notes whatever) in the extreme bass an octave lower. The reverberation from the strings thus set free is very like a subtle pedal effect. As such it does not carry far, but is quite perceptible in a small room. And the concert room is not the only or even the best place for such music.

[Note that in this 1986 re-issue, Craxton's detailed pedalling indications have been deleted. Not only do they tend to distract from the musical text – and from Beethoven's own markings – but it is felt preferable for the player to determine the degree of pedalling required, guided in some instances by Tovey's helpful advice.]

Slurs and Phrasing

The classical composers did not arrive at a coherent system of marks of articulation, and our modern efforts at such a system expose us to the risk of misinterpreting such traces of older systems that exist. The first point we must realise is that each type of instrument is likely to develop a system of its own, and the second point is that the pianoforte is of all instruments the most incapable of doing so. Articulation on the violin depends on the up-and-down of the bow. On wind instruments it depends on the breath and the tongue.

All these things have their natural habits and limits. Mozart and Beethoven knew better than to insist upon treating the articulation of a flute or oboe like the bowing of a violin; and when some pianoforte professor has reduced the phrasing of classical symphonies to uniformity, the intelligent conductor must spend hours with a blue pencil and a staff of copyists restoring the original practical common-sense of the composer. Articulation on the pianoforte and the organ has no natural limits, and most of its natural habits are bad. Some things that violins can do are impossible on the pianoforte, and some things have quite a different meaning on different instruments. Thus in the first movement of the *Eroica* Symphony the rhythm of

would lose all energy if the violinists bowed it as follows:

But on the pianoforte the latter form of slur is the only possible one. An attempt to separate the semiquavers from the following quavers would lead to a worse loss of energy than that which Beethoven's violin-bowing avoids. Yet Liszt, in his pianoforte arrangement of the *Eroica* Symphony, reproduces Beethoven's bowing on the assumption that no pianist will misunderstand it. In quiet passages we may find borderline cases, as in the Scherzo of Op.28.

There is no limit to the length of an unbroken pianoforte legato, and the instinct of composers from Beethoven to Wagner is to indicate as long an unbroken legato as possible, whatever means an instrument can use for concealing breaks. No sane musician supposes that Beethoven expected the player of his violin concerto to play four bars of moderate common time with a big tone in one bow, or that Wagner expected eight bars of the *Siegfried Idyll* to be played in one bow by the whole string band. What they required was that in such cases the players should conceal the inevitable changes. With pianoforte music the changes are not inevitable. Accordingly the only slurs that mean much are those over small groups. Mozart (when uninterfered with by the instructive-destructive editor) sometimes has significant slurs over as many as eight notes. Longer slurs are mere prescriptions for legato, and they have the disadvantage of being at the mercy of the width of page in both manuscript and print. Thus they may become deceptive. For example, Beethoven puts the first figure (a preliminary quarter and a whole bar) of the Op.57 Sonata under one slur. In the next phrase the same group seems to detach the first two notes from the rest. This is only because in old editions the title *Sonata Op.57* was set at the beginning of the line, so that there was room only for four full bars.

In the present edition the following points will show how far our phrasing may claim to be Beethoven's. 1. Editorial slurs have nothing to do with legato. When there are two slurs affecting the same notes, usually the shorter is Beethoven's. 2. Beethoven never makes two slurs meet, and therefore has no means of indicating the numerous cases in which he wishes to have no break between his phrases. 3. Short sub-phrase indications concern matters of touch, whereas our long slurs only show phrase-lengths. 4. Beethoven does not know of the *tenuto* line as the opposite of the staccato dot. Accordingly these features are editorial.

The present edition, then, does not claim the perfection that M. Bannelier describes as chimerical. But that chimerical perfection is not merely impossible because of human limitations. It does not exist even as a Platonic idea or a Beethovenish ideal. There is no reason why an edition should not claim to give only such readings as have survived Beethoven's own scrutiny, and to deal honestly with matters of doubt. Such claims may be made in various degrees of completeness. The present edition does not review the evidence for the selected reading except where to select only one reading would be to falsify a real doubt, as in the famous insoluble dilemma at the return in the first movement of Op.106. What is claimed here is that Beethoven would have no reason to complain that the editors have substituted their ideas for his. Mistakes there will be: but only because the infallible proof-reader does not exist.

DONALD FRANCIS TOVEY

SONATA in F minor, Op. 2 No. 1

Allegro

Bars 1–8   The statement of the theme is quiet at first, and does not rise to more than a melodic climax. Editors have suggested *sforzando* marks where Beethoven has none; but such additions assume, very mistakenly, that Beethoven means nothing by the contrast between this comparatively quiet opening and its angry recapitulation in bb.101–108.

bb.9–20   The chain of suspensions needs a good legato in all the semibreves, whether these are repeated or different notes. The analysis shows that the phrase-rhythm here becomes ambiguous. A hard accentuation will not clear it up; on the contrary, it will falsify it. When a new treble voice enters at b.11 it answers the second bar of the phrase in the bass voice. Think of it as a dramatic person, and ask yourself what it thinks it is doing. Is it answering that second bar as such, or is it starting a period of its own? Questions of this kind have some meaning in blank-verse drama when a line is distributed among several characters; but blank verse does not survive such treatment in long passages; and in sonata music square phrase-rhythm is not meant to survive it except by composers with a poor sense of form.

The general effect of this whole passage is that of a *crescendo*; but the *forte* reached in b.18 is of a kind that we may call *melodic*; not a percussion *forte* like that of the last chords of the whole movement. In Beethoven's early works, and on the pianoforte of his early days, even a *fortissimo* might be merely melodic.

b.62   The D in the seventh quaver of this bar should almost certainly be natural, though the key of C minor is not due till the next bar. Accidentals are one matter in which Beethoven is liable to oversights; and his early style is not in keeping with such obscurities as the fleeting conflict between D♭ and F♯ here. The ear cannot appreciate its point in quavers at this tempo. Still, though we may prefer D♮ and feel convinced that Beethoven meant it, we have no business to suppress the evidence of doubt.

bb.63–80   The cadential remarks in the treble at bb.69 & 71 should be played as things of serious weight. The theme in the bass is almost immediately reduced to a mere outline in syncopations answered by the minims in the treble. These are therefore continuing a dialogue which began at b.63.

bb.85–86   Here is a good opportunity for mastering the best of all short trills – viz.:

– the double triplet with a change of fingers. It is quite possible in full tempo here; but if you find it risky, you can omit the first note when you come to play in tempo. It is always easy to shorten a trill when you have mastered an extra length of it; but it is not so easy to improve a feeble trill.

bb.93–100   The young player can have no more delightful inducement to learn the possibilities of a good *pianissimo* touch and *crescendo* without discouraging technical difficulty, than this early and perfect specimen of Beethoven's art of dramatic delay.

bb.132–140   Apart from translation into the minor mode, these bars obviously differ from the corresponding bb.33–41; and the difference coincides with the fact that the three-spaced F was the top note of the pianoforte at the date of this sonata. But there is not the slightest reason to suppose that Beethoven would have troubled to reconcile the 'discrepancy' if the compass had been larger. Some editors have suggested that bb.33–41 ought to be altered in conformity with the present version. But why should not the present top F, which is aesthetically higher than the F as 6th of A♭ in b.37, have the advantage of thus producing an enhanced climax? In chamber music and symphonies Beethoven hardly ever writes a recapitulation without such changes, and in most cases these have nothing to do with the compass or technique of the instruments.

Adagio

Bar 1   Distinguish, carefully in your practising and naturally in your result, between the turn which comes before the second beat and the short grace-note which comes on the beat, but without accent.

bb.17–20   Do not force the tone in the melody. Nothing will prevent these bars from sounding thin, and on the early pianoforte nothing else was expected of them. But the thirds in the l.h. should stimulate the ambition for a fine legato with a singing tone in both parts; and the descents of the r.h. into the bass should be conceived as suggested by one of the favourite displays of the 18th-century singer – the exhibition of *Treffsicherheit*, or unerring accuracy in hitting notes at opposite limits of the voice; as in the following typical cadence:

Thus the bass-notes of the r.h. belong to the melody.

b.56   Though for convenience Beethoven divides this between the hands, it should be played as a single ornate melody. Get a first-rate violinist to play it to you in G, thus. It is not so easy for the violin as it is for the pianoforte; and so the violinist will take pains to play it beautifully.

At b.52 the first editions have various awkward readings of the bass. Our text is probably right, but Liszt's conjecture is musically very good:

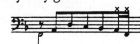

Menuet

The rhythm is ambiguous throughout; *i.e.,* if the first main accent is on b.1 the cadences become weak, and if it is on b.2 the later *sforzando* and *fortissimo* marks lie athwart it. For immediate purposes it suffices that such music needs no more hard accents than those which the composer indicates; that these indications are not only important but that additions to them are apt to destroy the sense (as is done by editors who add a *sforzando* to b.32); and that ambiguity and a tendency to shift must be accepted as positive qualities in the rhythms of classical music. The grace-notes are proved to be short by the fact that they are contrasted with full-sized quavers as a variation in bb.22–24.

Trio

Play this throughout as a piece of free double counterpoint, the crotchet theme being as important as the quaver theme, whichever of the two be above or below. The progression of whole-bar notes (C, B♮, B♭) in the second strain will need enough singing tone for the notes to last. But remember that a forced tone destroys legato in long notes, as the ear takes more notice of their diminution.

Prestissimo

Technically the most difficult thing in this sonata is the triplet passage for the l.h. at the outset of this finale. It makes a very good introduction to the study of pianoforte tremolos, but it is at the outset complicated by changes of position which add the problems of arpeggio playing. But the tremolo aspect is the most important and also, fortunately, the easiest. The student may begin with the following exercises:

The hand should move as little and as quietly as possible, especially when the thumb has to take the F. The fingering does not admit a perfect legato; but the student will find that evenness of tone goes a long way towards the effect of legato. Meanwhile the attempt to play this exercise evenly will reveal first what the positions of the hand really are in Beethoven's arpeggios, and, secondly, what a very small shift is needed to pass from one to the next.

Proceed from this exercise to the passage itself, aiming immediately at two things – perfect equality in all three notes of each triplet whatever the volume of tone, and, at the same time, a sharp contrast between the *piano* and the *forte*. Start your practice at a pace at which you can make sure of these points, and do not increase the pace until there is no risk of becoming less sure of them. Lastly, do not attempt the rest of the movement until you have mastered this opening. Some people think that the discouragement that comes of tackling Beethoven without proper practice is a useful experience. It is not.

This sonata will probably be attempted by players whose hands are so small that the second chord in the r.h. is troublesome. (Some of our greatest players have found it

so.) In any case, the student should treat such chord sequences in a way converse but analogous to that suggested here for the arpeggios – viz., first practise the chords legato, or perhaps in arpeggio –

and thus find out what is the minimum change of position for the hand and fingers before attempting to throw the chords from a height. If a note must be left out, leave out the G; the octaves are essential to the colour.

bb.59–108 Do not let this episode drag. Here, again, cultivate your l.h. and teach it to do a dance-rhythm that you yourself can enjoy for its tone and its lilt.

DONALD FRANCIS TOVEY

Dedicated to Joseph Haydn

SONATA
in F minor

BEETHOVEN, Op. 2 No 1

15

A. B. 232

18

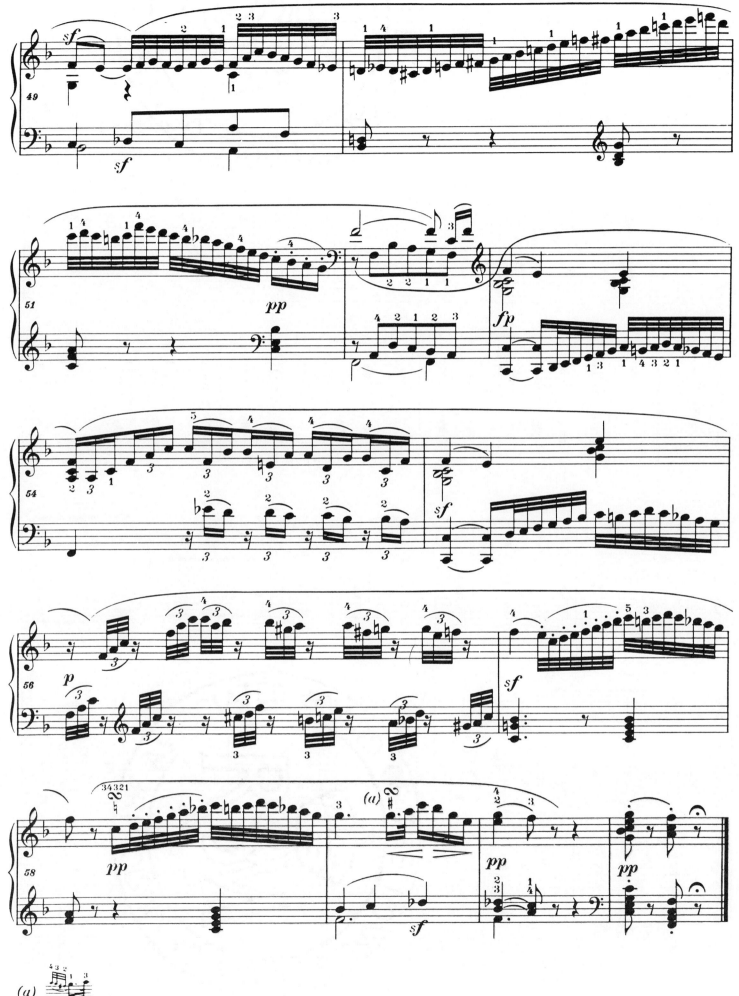

MENUETTO
Allegretto

TRIO

Menuet D.C.

24

Prestissimo

(a) As in first movement bar 85, or perhaps without a turn,

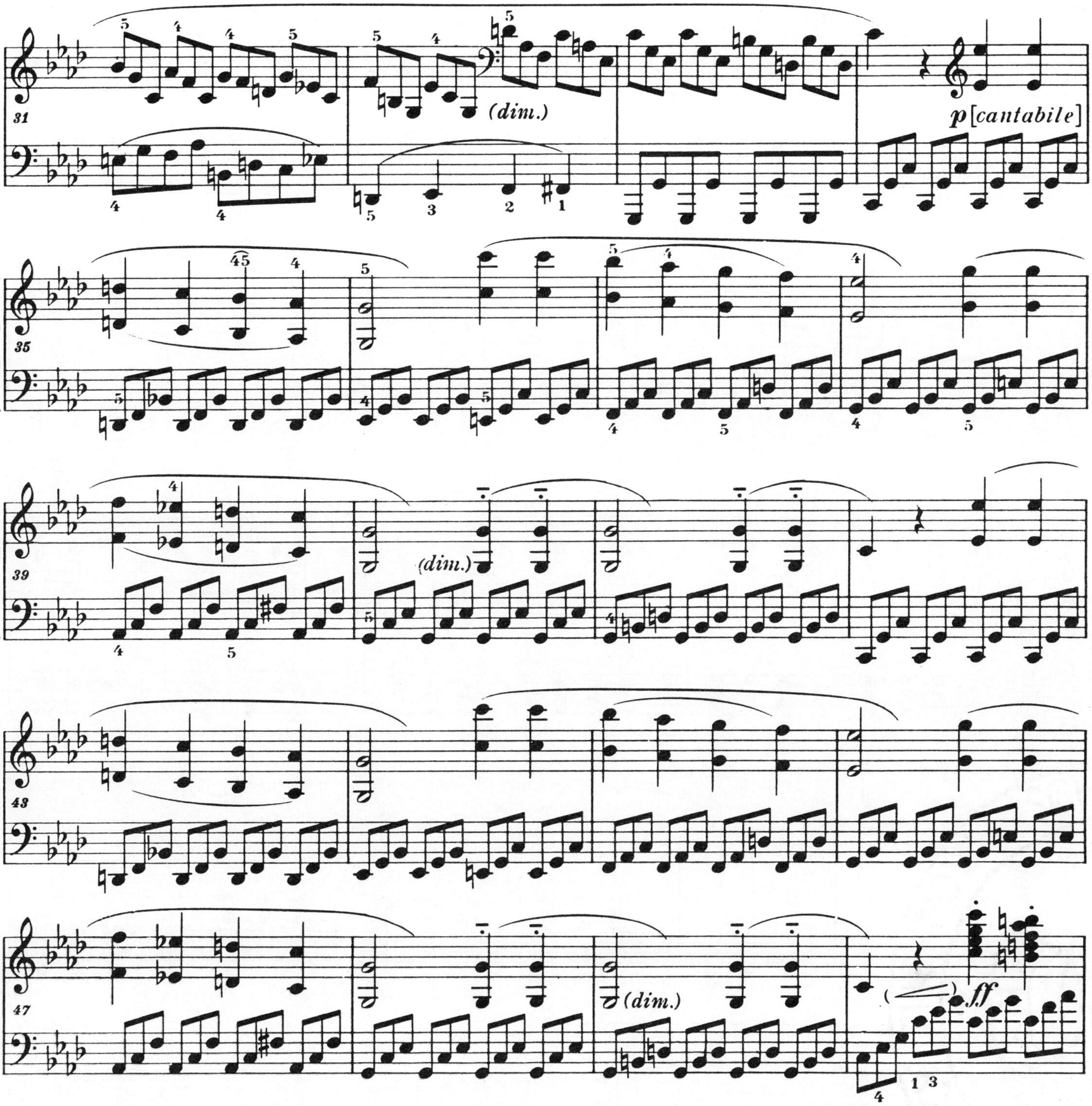
(dim.)
p [cantabile]
(dim.)
(dim.)
ff
ff
p
ff
ff

SONATA in A major, Op.2 No.2

Allegro Vivace

Beware of taking this movement too fast. The direction *vivace* describes the energy of the music, but the notation in crochets and quavers does not mean any such tempo as would make the triplet semiquavers unintelligible. Take your tempo from these, aiming at great brilliance and a big tone from the full height of the finger-fall. Even in bb.1 & 3, which are *piano*, the demisemiquaver in both hands should bristle with energy. The temptation to a dangerous tempo results from the tremolo bass of bb.58–75. The student should realise betimes that the tremolo, like its special case the trill, depends for its effect much more upon equality of tone and time than upon rapidity, and that it is at its best when the player is playing a definite number of notes. Here in bb.58–75 you will find that if you have always kept your notes even and regulated your *crescendo* note by note, the bass begins to sound continuous and dramatic at a pace you might have thought childishly cautious. The incidental details off the beat at each upward step, if mastered from the outset with the rest of the passage, greatly enhance its dramatic tone-colour. Players, young and old, too often despise such opportunities for developing a good rhythmically regular tremolo.

Bars 84 ff. The triplet octaves are characteristic of Beethoven's early pianoforte style. They are suited to a large hand, to which they are not much more difficult than 6ths. The fingering is Beethoven's own. If two hands are used (as here suggested), the player should avoid accentuating the l.h., and should accordingly use it at the ends of the rising triplets instead of at the beginning as in descending. The touch should, in short, be such as would be natural if the passage ran as follows:

Accordingly it is a mistake to attempt Beethoven's fingering if the hand is too small for a tolerable legato. But it is a worse mistake to give hard accents to the l.h.

b.104 Some editions published in Beethoven's lifetime add an upper minim E, corresponding to that in b.108 and to the A in the parallel passage at b.324. The parallel passage is no evidence, as the A is there necessary on other grounds. We are not obliged to assume that Beethoven noticed or consented to the E in b.104, and the entry of the minims is much better without it. According to one account it was the head of the *p* which happened to light upon the bottom line of the stave.

b.117 Beethoven marks both parts of this movement to be repeated. According to Mandyczewski, Beethoven intended to repeat the second part from b.121/2; and also to have a 2-bar silence at b.117, which is not very convincing. In public performance this highly dramatic movement is more impressive without repeats at all.

bb.181 ff. It shows the moderation of Beethoven's demands on other players, that though his early favourite broken-octave device shows that he could easily stretch 10ths, he never writes such a stretch as an unbroken chord, even under the temptation of such polyphony as we have here. The 'grace-notes' (a misnomer in this case) must have as much tone as the rest of the inner part which they represent, and must, of course, fall on the time as represented by the bass. The delay in the treble will not be noticed; whereas if the 'grace-notes' come before their time they will not be heard. Players with very large hands may take the 10th according to the sense – viz.:

Note that Beethoven *does* expect the player to stretch a 9th. The bracketed *tenuto* mark is not his; but he writes a crochet at the top and puts no staccato sign upon it. His intention is unmistakable.

Largo Appassionato

Bars 1–8 The technical task of the staccato bass cannot fail to fascinate the student. The chords above, l.h. included, must be religiously sustained, without gaps even between repeated notes. Learn betimes the beauty of their sound as reverberating *only* by contrast with the staccato bass, which does actually reinforce with its own harmonics each tonic chord like a very ethereal pedal. The gross mechanism of the ordinary pedal is therefore forbidden here. It must be reserved for the climax. It is not wanted even if you cannot stretch the 10th in b.3. On no account play that bass-note before the beat; put it exactly together with the right hand, and nobody will even suspect that the E has been delayed.

In the 3rd crotchet of b.3 there is no means of indicating that the D belongs to the staccato part as well as to the chord. Strange to say, its disappearance from the staccato part will not be missed unless you have been indiscreet enough to put a swell there. On the other hand, it absolutely must be held as a note of the chord.

bb.17–18 Much more difficult than any detail of this delightful task is the climax at bb.17–18. Before you attempt anything else in this movement, find out what your biggest tone amounts to in those bars, taking care that the melody dominates in every chord. With careful pedalling you may lift your hands without breaking the legato. Remember that a thunderous bass is worse than useless unless the treble (*not* a few chance inner notes) can dominate.

Having ascertained what you can do properly here, be contented with it and grade your *crescendo* up to it and not beyond. Your tone will grow if (and only if) you do not ruin your ear by letting it get used to ill-balanced chords and ugly qualities.

bb.9–13, 40–43 Beethoven's different beginnings to the trill show his sensitiveness to harmonic colour according to whether the melody is in the treble or the bass. The plain trill cannot follow the old rule of beginning with the upper note, for that has just been played. The grace-notes, on the other hand, are written in accordance with the old rule; *i.e.*, you are to play –

and no such hiccough as –

Scherzo

The semiquaver figure is very difficult, especially in the left hand, where you had certainly better 'change feet' on the middle step, as you may find easier to do in the right hand. Do not begin by trying to make it glitter; the glitter will come from inveterate accuracy in slow practice with attention to the precise (and *minimum*) movement of the hand. An 'agogic accent' (which the brutal truth calls a drag) on the first note is detestable. On the other hand, do not flick off the crotchet: let it sing, though the softer the better. Eventually (but not before long practice) the tempo should be quite lively, with no stodginess in b.3. Some passion is then possible in the Trio, where Beethoven's phrasing (1 + 1 + 1 + 1 + 4) should be respected and the first 4 bars treated as a dialogue.

Rondo

The unusual use of *grazioso* merely as a tempo mark almost suffices to suggest the right pace, which is hardly above *andante*. Semiquavers should flow gently. Too slow a tempo would need a jerk forward into a quicker time for the A minor episode. On the other hand, most people are apt to take that kind of episode far too fast; few players without special information have any idea of the weight of Beethoven's staccato *fortissimos*. They belong to the resources in which the early pianoforte sounded formidable because it was obviously displaying its full strength, whereas the modern pianoforte sounds weak in them because it can make much more noise in other ways.

Accordingly the first thing to practise in this movement is bb.56–99, with the inflexible ambition to express every contrast clearly. The rhythms in the left hand need as much energy as the hail-storm in the right. Persons who are accustomed to no loud staccato less heavy than *martellato* octaves should realise that a hail-storm is more sublime than a coal-shoot in use. When you have learnt to command the stinging tone of this episode you will find that you need not take it any faster than will join smoothly on to the deliberate flow of the *grazioso*; and that if the *grazioso* will not join on to your majestic hail-storm it probably will also fail to flow in itself.

After you have mastered this problem you can attend to finer details. In b.1 you learn (for the first time in Beethoven's Sonatas, taken chronologically) that when Beethoven writes an arpeggio or scale in an irregular number of notes (eleven here) he knows exactly how to divide it; and that if you do anything different your result will be dull. Study each variant of this theme accurately according to Beethoven's directions. Every time you think he has brought the wrong note on to the beat or hurried in the middle instead of at the end, or done other things that would never have occurred to you, the result, when you have got it in *tempo*, will have a sparkle that nothing else could give. Of course, all the notes must be there.

The portamento in b.2 is one of those things which violinists and singers are supposed to do well and pianists not at all. As a matter of fact, the pianoforte can suggest the effect (by balance of tone) much better than the violin can realise it across the strings. It is true, and on the whole fortunate, that the pianoforte cannot slither; but nothing in all Chopin or Liszt suits it better than b.2 of this movement played with a swoop of the wrist down to the thumb on G♯, and all in a quiet tone. Persons who hit the top E smartly, as with a thimble, had better leave music and music-lovers in peace.

Bar 100 A little judicious pedal, at regions selected by experience of each individual pianoforte, will give the student timely opportunity to learn how to listen to his own playing as well as to the criticisms of his teacher. Of course, this does not belong to the stage at which the scale is still being mastered as an even series of notes. But after that stage it is as mistaken to remain contented with dryness as to put up with messiness.

bb.159–160 In early works Beethoven often uses the *ff* mark in purely melodic climaxes without percussion. But while you must avoid percussion in such places, you must not ignore this evidence that his early style was to him anything but a placid imitation of Mozartean smoothness. In the present case, though the climax is melodic, it leads straight back to the 'hail-storm'.

b.180 The last 8 bars must not be hustled, and a good indication of the general tempo may be found in the fact that the cross-slurring of these semiquavers will need a little slackening. Obviously the staccato of the following descending scale has nothing of the hail-storm quality about it.

DONALD FRANCIS TOVEY

Dedicated to Joseph Haydn

SONATA
in A

BEETHOVEN, Op. 2 No. 2

Allegro vivace

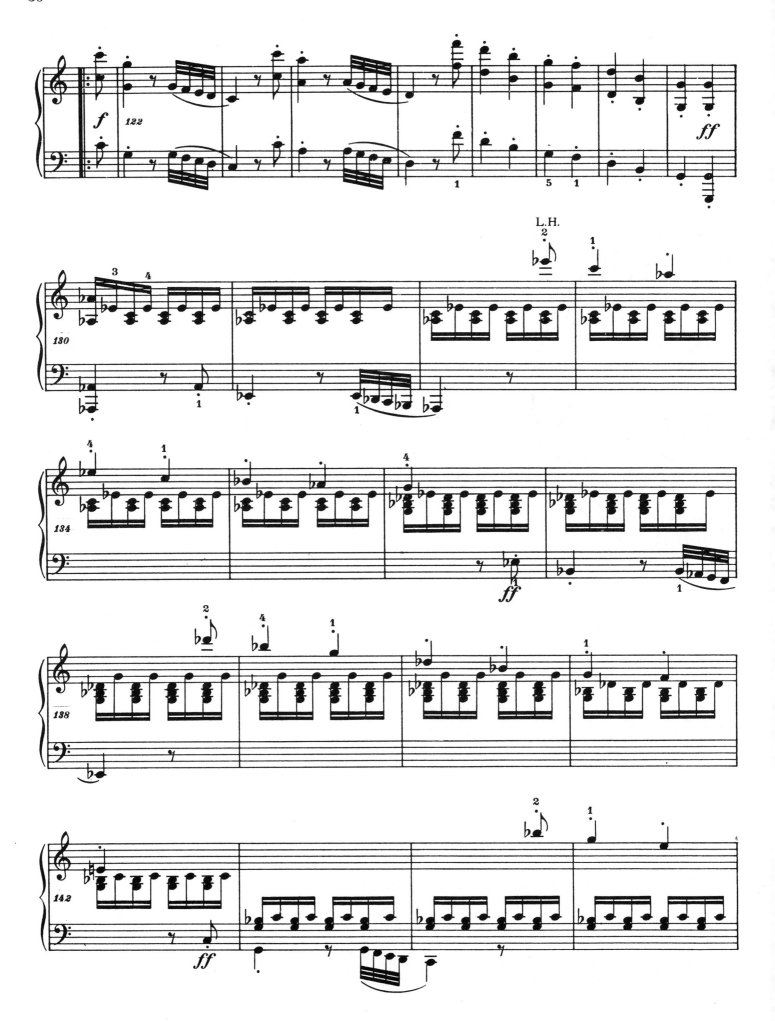

Largo appassionato

SCHERZO
Allegretto

Trio

Scherzo D. C.

RONDO
Grazioso

SONATA in C major, Op.2 No.3

Allegro con brio

The tempo, though in no way suggestive of *alla breve*, should be fast enough to give the utmost brilliance to the semiquaver passages. The demisemiquavers in bb.22 & 24 are no hindrance; they lie so that firm fingers can dash over them with great ease.

Bar 3 Tenths are less rare in Beethoven's early works than in his later. Beethoven himself puts the fingering $\frac{1B}{5G}$, showing that he expects this tenth to be taken by l.h. alone. Many hands that cannot take a tenth by direct attack can easily take it over if it has been prepared by another hand. If r.h. takes the B it will have to let it go before attacking the semiquavers in thirds. If the left thumb cannot then reach it without letting the bass go, then we must be content to let the B vanish, as pedal will blur the semiquavers. Anything is better than the miserable practice of playing G before the beat, hopping up to the B and then putting down the pedal when the G has hopelessly vanished. Always get your bass-note on the beat and into whatever pedal is necessary. And always judge of these things by ear. Listen for what you want, and hear that you get it. Whatever happens, this G must last through the bar.

bb.13, 61 etc. The pedal should not long retain the bass chord, but should be changed at each upward step.

b.15 Keep the quavers in a heavy non-legato and do not slur them in pairs. Beethoven does not want such things when he does not indicate them.

b.27 Never let a turn become quite stiff, as .
Here a broad  or even ♩♪♫ will be good.

b.45 Beethoven's incorrect notation of this figure occurs in other early works. It has the merit of showing that in his intention the grace-notes are to fill out an even quaver; whereas the correct notation ♪♩♪ may mean anything. But there is a good deal to be said for the alternative interpretation:

The following reading is correct:

bb.56, 58, 59 Get a better *Pralltriller* than the commonplace triplet of semiquavers. The trill at the end of 59 is well represented by ♫ *i.e.,* 4 demisemiquavers without a turn.

b.69 Bring out the contrast between the legato, or nearly legato, syncopations and the staccato chords above them.

bb.73-75 Make the exact rhythm clear. This is easy, as the beats fall on the thumb. But you need big tone in the other fingers too.

bb.76-77 The use of three *fortes* in succession does not mean fussiness on Beethoven's part, nor does it mean *fff*. It means that Beethoven relies on normal accentuation as a rule (viz., that the first beat is heavier than the third, and that the third is heavier than either the second or the fourth), but that we have here a cadence in which all three accents (first, third, and first) should be equal. If he had been able to take advantage of some modern rhythmic theories he would have expressed this correctly by going into $\frac{2}{4}$ time. And then our tidy editors would have corrected this back again.

b.78 The group  provides a good trill, especially with this change of fingers.

bb.85–88 When broken octaves are as conjunct as this it is always good to feel your way along the top with the outside fingers (and along the bottom in the l.h.), keeping your muscles loose. In your practising you should also sometimes imagine the groups shifted a note forward or backward, as ♫ etc. This reveals weaknesses and gives opportunity to repair them.

At b.88 do not extend the broken octaves downwards in the l.h. Even a pianoforte that goes down to A does not go far enough, and its bottom notes are too dark for rapid movement. Beethoven abandons his figure at the best point here. The parallel passage in C major at the end of the movement is another matter, and will sound very well if carried down to the bottom C.

bb.97–108 This passage does not imply the hard dabs of the thumb with which it is commonly played. Such execution feels vigorous, but sounds thin. Remember the evidence that Beethoven could stretch a tenth. If you have no such stretch you can feel how this passage ought to be played by trying a legato in the following scheme, gathering up your hand in the middle of each position:

Now this is not to be taken as a substitute for the text. It merely shows you what colour you can produce with a large enough hand. If your hand is small, what you now have to do is to rely on the pedal for the bass chords (which should have a fine contrafagotto growl, not a mere coal-shoot crash) and to take the thumb-note with the l.h.

bb.107–108 The only really difficult corner is at the *calando*, where the pedal must not become messy and the bass chord cannot be released. At the end of the finale the contrast between *calando* and *rallentando* forbids us to slacken the pace. *Calando* means much the same as *mancando* – *i.e.,* failing or fainting. Practise these in a legato and an even tone in all rhythmic phases, especially the following:

etc.

b.129 Beethoven assigns the A to r.h., evidently finding it easy to do the semiquavers with left index finger and thumb, but not with the middle finger as well. This is interesting evidence of the size and shape of his hand; but it is no reason why we should not use the r.h. from the second semiquaver. To take the whole group in r.h. might lead to clipping the crotchet figure ungracefully.

bb.143–144   In memorising this sonata do not forget the difference in the bass between this and bb.5–6. In itself it is not important; but players who take to levelling down these 'discrepancies' very soon destroy what capacity they may once have had for understanding Beethoven's style.

bb.147–153   Apart from Beethoven's articulation of the quavers  this syncopated counterpoint should be a close legato in contrast with the staccato thematic figure, except in the last bar (154) where the quavers of l.h. are in sympathy with those of r.h.

b.213   The *rinforzando*, instead of the *piano* of b.79, is an enhancement natural here where we are about to plunge into the Coda. Do not, therefore, alter either it or b.80.

bb.218–232   On no account either hurry or drag this grandiose passage. It is not as grand as the big expanses in Beethoven's later works; but we do not improve the ambitious passages of a young artist by taking them less seriously than he did before he knew better. The pedal needs no change for the whole six bars of A♮ chord. Do not begin the *crescendo* before Beethoven marks it.

b.232   Here is an opportunity for learning how to play cadenzas. Some students ask for an edition in which such passages are written out in full-sized notes, chopped into ordinary bars by machinery. Their trouble is that they do not want to learn music, but simply to be taught a set of parlour tricks. Cadenzas, of all forms of music, ought to sound as if they were extemporised. Where there are any regular bars to be found in the present cadenza, good playing will conceal them. Where there is any irregularity, good playing will make a point of it.

The preliminary uprush in grace-note semiquaver groups cannot be too quick. Hard accents and a deliberate beginning will only make it dull and pedantic. We do not want to notice that there are just eight crotchet-loads of these groups. The chief weight of tone is needed for the high E to which they lead. If this is not to sound hard the uprush should have begun quite *piano* (that is why Beethoven marks *fp* on the previous chord), and there will thus be room for a fine *crescendo*. Now comes a remarkable point. If the top E were a minim we should be beginning the first theme, with a pause over its first note. But not only has Beethoven written the E as a crotchet, but he has removed all possibility of its being a misprint by putting a crotchet rest in the bass. The E is merely the top of the uprush of grace-notes with which a solo player emerges from the grand cadential ⁶₄ chord of the orchestra. The serious declamatory business begins now, and takes the form of a duet. After the pause on E, begin well under tempo. Let the l.h. enter as an answering voice. Do not hurry beyond such a tempo as will allow a distinct colouring of A minor to be felt in the third and fourth steps. When you reach the groups beginning on C♯, make a rhetorical point of the difference between those that rise to E and those that rise to F; make this point wistfully, not naggingly, and continue to make it even when the semiquavers become unbroken. Increase the pace just as far as

these points will permit, and leave room for a distinction between the last semiquavers and the indefinitely rapid trill. In Beethoven's time it was not necessary to indicate that this trill should begin on the upper note.

Adagio
The tempo of the first theme can hardly be too slow for b.10; and the rests must be as exactly in time as the notes. Count 8; a demisemiquaver has quite a melodic meaning, especially the B♯ in b.10.

Bars 11–42   The claims of the first theme must be reconciled with the need for flow throughout all the passages covered by the demisemiquaver figure. Good playing will accomplish this compromise by an actual difference of tempo which, however, will not be felt as a contrast. To attain this you must first have mastered the expression of every detail in a tempo slow enough for b.10. Then, and not till then, will you find yourself swinging naturally into the best rhythm for each passage. But if you start with the crude notion of *più mosso* or *accelerando*, you will achieve nothing but sentimental rubato and perfunctoriness where Beethoven demands breadth. The l.h. has the theme throughout, and is always legato. When the l.h. is crossed over the right the pedal should not prolong the bass-notes to more than a quaver, or the inner harmonies will become messy. Like bb.17–20 of the Adagio of Op.2 No.1, bb.16–17 etc. of this passage will never sound rich in tone; and the effort to force the tone will only make them thinner.

At b.26 we may unhesitatingly take the low E, which was not on Beethoven's pianoforte until 1822 or so. Nottebohm and Mandyczewski opine that in bb.31 & 34 (why not also in b.28?) the *piano* should come *after* the first beat. This is very probably right; but do not 'lead up' to Beethoven's sudden *ff* in b.26 or elsewhere. If you do not like his style, why study Beethoven at all?

b.74   The first turn may have a B♯. But do not put C✗ into the second turn.

b.80   The trill is best with a turn, with B♯.

Scherzo: Allegro
Two things should deter the student from forcing the pace: first, that the three-quaver figure in the Scherzo must on no account ever suggest a triplet, and, secondly, that the *sf* chords at the ends of bb.29, 31 etc. must have time to speak and must not be wiped out (as most players are apt to obliterate them) by equally strong accents on the beat. Treat bb.33/34–36 as a 3-bar group, answered by 36/37–39; and show the distinction between the expiring *pp* and the daylight *piano* of the returning major theme.

Trio
The *sforzandos* in the second part must not be applied to the first part. See analysis in *A Companion to Beethoven's Pianoforte Sonatas** for the demonstration that the rhythm at the beginning of the Trio starts on a main bar, but that

* *A Companion to Beethoven's Pianoforte Sonatas: A Complete Book of Analyses.* (Associated Board)

in the second part it changes step, mainly with the help of the new *sforzandos*. Moreover, do not supplement these anywhere else in the sequel. It is disastrous to assume, without overwhelming evidence, that Beethoven does not mean exactly what he writes.

Count the rests exactly, both in returning to the Scherzo and proceeding to the Coda.

Allegro assai

Assai originally meant the same as *assez*. Both in Italian and French the same ironical process has caused these equivalents of 'pretty fast' to suggest extremes. Never lose sight of the literal meaning, and be content to take *Allegro assai* 'fast *enough*'.

Bar 3 Mind the C in the last quaver: you will never develop a keen ear if you are content to play  instead.

bb.8–18 These bars will fix the tempo for you. Until you can prevent them from sounding like double triplets you will spoil your playing by attempting this movement in anything like tempo. The touch needed here is that of Mendelssohn's so-called *Spinnerlied*. Imagine bb.9–10 etc. thus:

It would be a mistake to *write* them thus, because it is a cardinal law of good expression-marks that they should not include what is implicit in the elements of notation and rhythm, but should be confined to what cannot be ascertained without them. Here we are not concerned, like Mendelssohn in the *Spinnerlied*, to bring out a melody apart from its accompaniment, but to get the right accentuation of a semiquaver theme which slovenly playing will turn into this:

Beethoven slurs the short groups, meaning thereby to indicate clear articulation, but not distortion or roughness. The main theme is marked *piano*, and this will have to be distinguished from the *pianissimo* two bars before each return after the principal episodes (67–68 & 179–180). Otherwise the softer the theme the better. It should suggest the inimitable staccato of flutes.

b.24 The best trill consists of four demisemiquavers played by three fingers . Do not attack it before its time. A delay of the beginning of the next bar will not be noticed, but a beginning too soon always sounds inept.

b.67 Do not put a slur at the beginning of this bar to correspond with those in bb.63 & 65. The sense is different. Those bars drifted out of a legato passage. We are now certain of the approach of the main theme.

b.79 The omission of a *piano* to match that in b.83 is probably an oversight.

bb.87–95 This is the most difficult passage in the sonata. A good method of attack is to master both hands together with absolute accuracy and fluency, but *omitting the outlying bass notes*. Having thus mastered everything in the l.h. which goes with the r.h., you should then practise the following l.h. groups:

and so on. The upward skips are easier; the main difficulty is in the downward ones. When these have been mastered the whole passage will probably come together at a moderate pace which can be rapidly and safely practised up to tempo. Never expect that wrong notes will gradually weed themselves out. They will only root themselves in. There is always a safe pace at which they need never occur. Keep the whole passage at this pace, instead of hurrying the easier parts. Regard a wrong note as a signal forbidding you to increase the pace to the next degree of the metronome until you have made the note correct *in its context*. Remember that there is no sense in correcting a note by itself. A wrong note means two wrong intervals, one before it and one after.

Do not force the tone. The passage is probably *forte*, but it is the loudness of argumentative voices, not of a bombardment. Beethoven has certainly neglected his markings somewhere in this neighbourhood. Probably a *diminuendo* is required from b.96 to the *pianissimo*; but there would be no great harm in beginning it earlier so as to end the staccato passage lightly.

b.100 It is well to complete the l.h. design in this bar now that the pianoforte has the notes. Bar 101 is the proper place for changing the pattern, which Beethoven does not wish to continue.

bb.103–118 Beethoven's phrasing in groups of four notes is not casual, and it is intended to be changed at bb.155–167, where the theme moves towards the home tonic.

The legato octaves at bb.111–116 (*N.B., not* legato at the cadence-bar 117) are far more difficult than they look. Join them carefully with pedal, but also with fingers on the following scheme, which illustrates Brahms's rule that in rising we bind the upper notes and in falling the lower:

Note that in the conjunct descent the thumb can easily glide with a perfect legato.

bb.191, 195 Do not put any *piano* here. The passage is not intended to match that in bb.79–83. That passage was drifting away from home; this one is triumphantly asserting the tonic.

b.196 Possibly the omission of a *piano* mark here is not accidental. At all events there would be no harm in this being louder than in bb.8–18.

bb.257 ff. No *crescendo*, please! Let the *fortissimo*, both in the trill and in the theme, come as a surprise, and keep it up throughout its four bars. Then you will not need to force the tone.

bb.269–278 Beethoven has not told us all his intentions here, and the bracketed *cresc.* is conjectural. A merely sudden *ff* at b.279 is certainly not his intention. Note that the point of the three *ff* marks is the same as that of the three *fortes* in the first movement at bb.76, 77: we are to give three equal accents, without distinction between main and subordinate. Contrast the last three bars of this movement, where 310 needs far more stress than 311.

bb.281–287 The sforzando in 285 explains itself on the assumption that Beethoven means the *pianos* in 283 and 287 to be sudden.

DONALD FRANCIS TOVEY

Dedicated to Joseph Haydn

SONATA
in C

BEETHOVEN, Op. 2 No. 3

Allegro con brio

(a) or

A. B. 234

(legato as possible)

Adagio

(see notes)

(ben legato)

Trio

SONATA in E flat major, Op.7

Allegro molto e con brio

The first thing to practise in this movement is the very difficult passage bb.111–127 and its parallel 291–307. This requires full tone in every note, with extreme rapidity. You must not, of course, begin by aiming at the rapidity, nor, indeed, by forcing the tone. First secure equal strength in all the notes. (Defects usually occur at the end of each group of 6.) Do not keep the thumb down; on the contrary, lift it as if in a staccato and swing away immediately (with a turn of the wrist) so as to throw weight into the little finger. Take as far as the first half of b.119 as one lap; then make a second lap from the other half of the bar to 127. Having treated this and the parallel passage 291-306 as a preliminary exercise, add to it the previous theme 93–111 and 273–291, making in your practising a clear distinction between the rapid 1-bar *crescendo* from *p* to *ff* in 97–98 and the 4-bar *crescendo* in 105–108. Do not be satisfied with commonplace triplets for the *Pralltriller* in 109–110, but aim immediately at the sharpest ornament you can get with three fingers, beginning always on the beat (*never* before it), but having the accent on the last note:

Two more passages of outstanding difficulty are the staccato of bb.49–54, mentally confusing to the two hands if attacked rashly, and detestable if unrhythmically played; and the beautiful legato octaves of bb.85–91, where Beethoven's phrasing is much more carefully thought out than any possible tidying up, the l.h. in b.87 being affected by the new design in the right so that it no longer conforms to b.83. The 1-bar slurs in 90–91 mark a middle stage before the staccato of the cadence-bar 92.

When these passages have been mastered the rest of the movement is easy. But do not on that account take it any faster than you can take the most difficult passages.

The tempo which will finally make an impression of irresistible onrush is that which nothing can hurry and nothing can delay. The impression depends partly on accent. A heavy and invariable second accent in the bar will make the fastest tempo sound dragging. Beethoven's *sforzandos*, if you do not obliterate them by adding others, contribute much to the sense of movement. Study the analysis,* especially in regard to the varying lengths of the phrases, noting in particular how the present extremely terse opening streams out in broadening lines.

Bar 1   Most editions agree in reading *p* here, but Nottebohm and Mandyczewski saw reason to believe that Beethoven intended *f*. In many ways this is better; but no conclusive evidence has been given for it.

bb.25–26; 29–30–33–34   The unsupported second chord will need as much tone as the first. The *sforzando* chords in 33–34, though loud, are not in the dramatic *ff* of the others; the move in the bass will help to distinguish them as two separate *sforzandos* instead of the unbroken figure (a) of the theme.

bb.39–40   Beware of the common mistake of treating the staccato notes as hard accents. On the contrary, their

* *A Companion to Beethoven's Pianoforte Sonatas: A Complete Book of Analyses.* (Associated Board)

proper effect is to throw a cross-accent on to the slurs.

bb.67–70   Do not let the inner part become confused with the melody. Regard this effect

as a blunder worse than any wrong note.

bb.72 & 252   The semitones (E♮, E♭; and later A♮, A♭) have probably no better authority than a rough conjecture that assumes that Beethoven is repeating b.64 (or 244). It is far more likely that Beethoven is anticipating (or starting) the future course of the passage.

b.136   The repeat is very necessary, otherwise the short first group will hardly establish the tonic.

b.214   There is no early authority for reading G♭. But G♮ is difficult to understand, and Beethoven is apt to omit necessary accidentals.

bb.333–335   The inverted pedal, though apparently forced on Beethoven by the fact that his instrument only reached F, is a detail no competent critic would alter. The *forte* sequel actually depends on the context not having risen above E♭ beforehand.

bb.351–354   Note, and express in your *crescendo*, the fact that the theme now begins on a 'weak' bar. See analysis.

bb.357–359   Play the progression in the bass clearly, marking the steps in b.358 with changes of pedal, but do not attempt an exaggerated accent on the B♭ and G, for you cannot in any case emphasise the whole sense – viz.:

because the very important upper E♭ is masked by the D.

Largo, con gran espressione

Mr Plunket Greene's first rule of song-singing applies throughout this wonderful and most solemn movement. *Sing through your rests.*

Learn to play the theme legato without tying the repeated notes. Early editors showed their own low standards of legato by adding ties.

Bars 10, 12, 15   If you cannot stretch tenths be sure to put the bass-note on the beat, together with the other hand, and also together with the new pedal. Then swing up to the tenth as quickly as possible. You need not hurry; to swing as quickly as possible is not to jerk viciously at the impossible. As habit produces confidence your tenths will soon be as close as the best violin chords of 3 or 4 notes. At least four of the greatest pianists now living cannot *strike* tenths, though their stretch is believed to be enormous! Be sure that the minims are held their full length by hand or pedal.

bb.10–12 etc.   Never let broad turns like this become stiff. Aim at something like 𝄞, or 𝄞

bb.20–21   The second chord of each three will need a

deliberately intended accent or the listener will lose the rhythm even if your rests are the correct length. It would be wrong to *write* this accent, because its object is merely to make the normal rhythm clear, and if it succeeds in doing this it will not be noticed at all, whereas a written mark implies something that attracts attention.

bb.25–36 Listen to the pizzicato of a good violoncello player in the slow movements of Op.59 No.1, and Op.59 No.3, to fire your ambition to play this properly. Remember that pedal, except for the actual length of a semiquaver on the first of each bar, and occasional help to legato of melody, will absolutely ruin your staccato. You will not *feel* this as you rejoice in your wrist action, but the listener will simply not know the difference between your best staccato and your stickiest playing if you take any but the rarest and shortest pedals. The legato chords, moreover, acquire bass-notes than from open pedal.

Of course, you can use a close *legatissimo* and pedal on every quaver in b.32.

bb.37–41 This is beyond the capacity of any pianoforte, and you must play what is written and trust that your listeners will see that you are in earnest and will share in your imagination. Put the grace-notes on the beat and do not take them faster than triplet demisemiquavers. In b.41 the difference between the *tenuto* crotchets and the previous quavers must be represented by an increase of tone. The mere use of pedal is not enough, for the pedal must not prolong the bass, and as late as 1890 few pianofortes had dampers above B.

b.45 It is often suggested that r.h. should enter in octaves now that the pianoforte goes high enough. And pray why should this passage not have three entries, although two of the voices afterwards go into octaves?

b.47 If you catch yourself playing a double dot here, or, on the other hand, failing to enjoy the reverberation of the top A♮ after the chord below has lasted out its quaver-length, regard either of these errors as the darkness before the dawn of your musical sense.

b.89 The proper tempo of the movement is so slow that very little, if any, slackening is desirable for this turn. In fact, this bar may be taken as a test of the tempo, of the whole, though the material of the A♭ theme will probably have needed some concession to keep it flowing.

Take the turn as a broad triplet

Do not be afraid of Beethoven's *ffp*. Though it is not a percussion effect, a certain violence is quite in character.

Allegro

Bars 12–15 Do not imagine that you can get these bars into shape by instinct. The silence must be measured.

bb.70–79 Be careful that the second crotchet of each bar is strong enough to show that it belongs to the melody and not merely to the accompaniment.

bb.86–95 Bar 86 is an accented bar, and the theme is in the bass, beginning on the second crotchet, and answered in double counterpoint at b.90.

Minore

This is perhaps the hardest passage in the sonata. Get an absolutely even tone in all notes of each triplet in both hands. Do not treat the tune as

but as

Beware of too much pedal when the harmony moves quickly. Find out what you can sustain with your fingers (*legatissimo*) before committing yourself to the pedal at all.

Beethoven's violent *ffp* marks are not to be expurgated.

Bars 146–149 See that this leads in strict time back to the beginning.

Rondo poco allegretto e grazioso

The tempo is a leisurely 4-in-a-bar for which *andante* would not be misleading. As in the first movement of Op.14 No.2, we are dealing with a late phase of an early style, where the detail is rich and the mood is ruminating. In the first movement of this sonata, on the other hand, we are dealing with an early phase of a later style, where impulses press urgently and run away with the tempo over wide ranges.

The hardest passage is the C minor episode, especially at bb.68–69, 85–86, 88–89. But a close legato is not necessary, so long as the tone is full. There is no harm in hopping with the little finger of r.h. from the first group to the second. Take care that in this C minor episode the *sf* chords off the main beat are not obliterated by equally loud main beats. A student who does not need this warning must be unusually sure that he can hear his own playing as others hear it.

When the stormy C minor theme becomes a heavenly calm in the home tonic at the end of the sonata, see that you play no *sforzando* except where Beethoven has marked them; and do not spoil the exquisite punctuality of the end by a sloppy *ritardando*.

One naturally wishes to alter bb.42–46 to match 135–139, where the compass of the pianoforte allows Beethoven to go a little higher in E♭. It is by no means certain that Beethoven would have made the passages exactly parallel whatever the compass of the instrument. The end of b.42 is as good a moment for getting rid of the trill as the next bar; and bb.135–139 are the better for being an enhanced variation of the original. Again, why not go an octave higher from the end of 135, to match the rise in 42? The Slough of Despond and the Serbonian Bog will be drained before all such possibilities are exhausted.

With the exception of the *Pralltriller*, which cannot be too close (C. P. E. Bach says 'it must really *prallen*', sc. 'bristle'), the ornaments should be broad; the turn ~ a

leisurely group of 5

DONALD FRANCIS TOVEY

Dedicated to the Countess Babette von Keglevics

SONATA
in E flat

BEETHOVEN. Op.7

(a) See notes

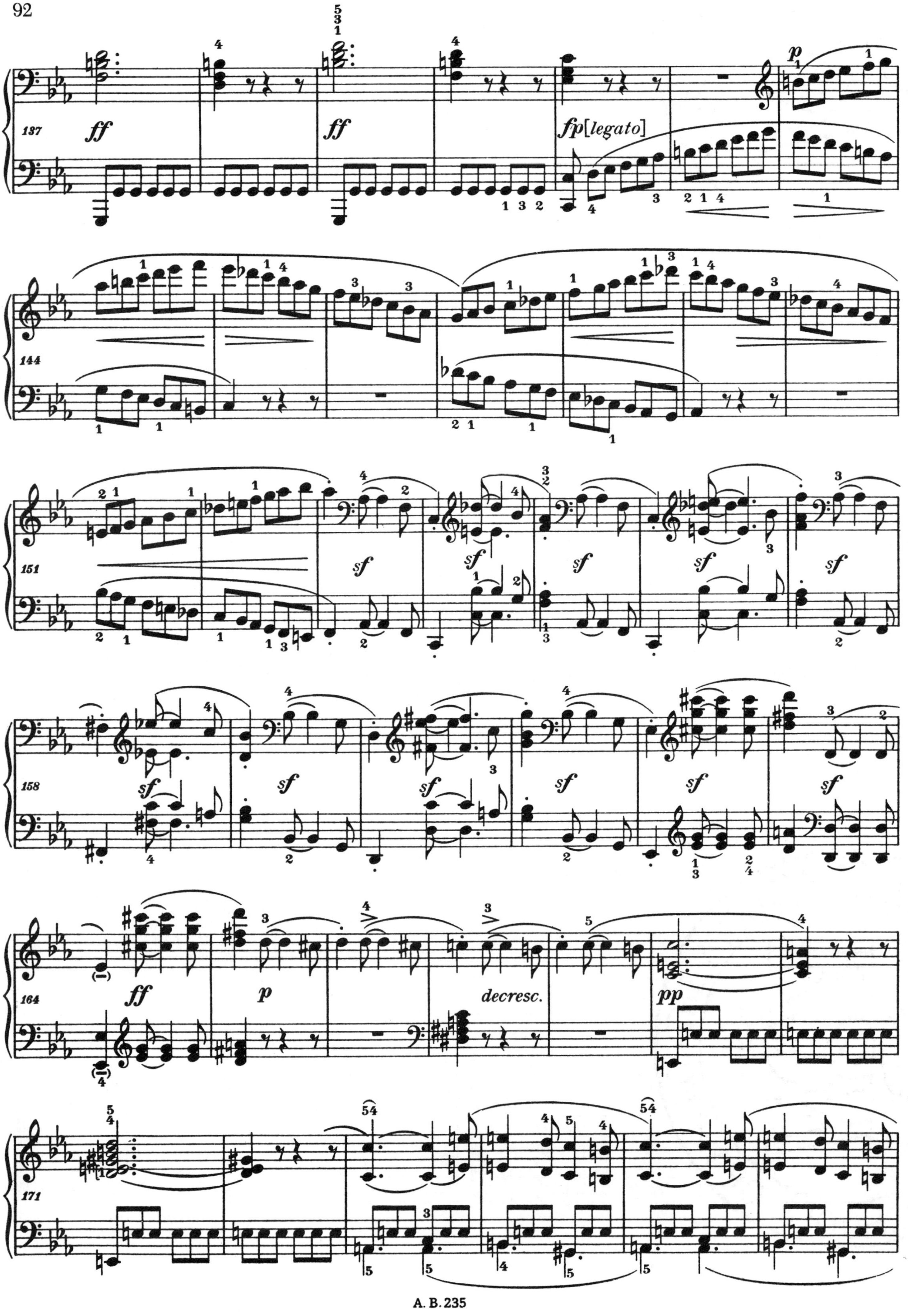
ff
fp[legato]
p
sf
decresc.
pp

(a) See notes

(a) This note is an octave higher in the original

A. B. 235

Largo, con gran espressione

Allegro

Minore

Allegro D. C.

RONDO
Poco Allegretto e grazioso

SONATA in C minor, Op.10 No.1

Allegro molto e con brio

The tempo is fast enough to make it inconvenient to count three, but it is not the one-in-a-bar of a scherzo. Note that the *forte* chords are not short, a dotted crotchet being half a bar, so that the following figure is only just separated from the chord. Attend to Beethoven's legato slurs and staccato dashes. Nothing could be more trivial than to

allow the rhythmic figure to break into  etc.

Analysis shows that between b.9 and b.16 the rhythm has changed step, so that bb.16 & 18 are the leaders of their pairs. So do not imagine that you can get the dramatic silences right by instinct. They must be counted.

After b.31 the jerky phrasing yields to a calmer flow, and from b.56 onwards the flow is grandly urgent until it subsides in the cadence-group, bb.94–105.

Find out how much tone you can develop at b.94 by practice; and then, knowing this to be the real climax, regulate the previous *crescendos* so that they do not overwhelm it. If you already make all the noise you can at b.84 you will have deflated your climax.

Bars 60–61 Here the turn is conceived as if the B♭ had been tied – *i.e.*, it belongs to the first bar

bb.82–83 Emphasise the difference between these bars and their variation in 84–85.

bb.110, 114 The bracketed *pianos* seem a necessary precaution when so many rash editors and teachers ignore the plain evidence of the light chords and insist on making this passage like the opening. The student cannot too soon or too often learn that Beethoven positively dislikes uniformity except where it is absolutely necessary to make things intelligible. The continued *pianos* in these chords are as essential a feature as the new harmony and tonality.

b.136 Follow Beethoven's phrasing as his slurs indicate expanding groups in the bass.

b.158 The bass will mark its rhythm with a soft drum-like staccato, while the chords above are detached gently with singing tone, *sospirando*.

b.161 The beautiful reading ⟨music⟩ (with C instead of A♭) has been corrupted by uniformitarians who want b.161 to tally with b.165. Exactly the same stupidity has made others object that if we read C in b.161 we ought to read it in b.165. Nothing has any intrinsic meaning with such commentators, and with them nothing can change as it grows: form is the symmetry produced by folding your paper in two while the ink is wet.

Beethoven may just as well write C at 161 and A at 165 as make bb.162–167 a couple of bars longer than bb.158–161. The most fanatic uniformitarian cannot explain away those two bars, and why should not the divergence at 165 be their point of origin?

Adagio molto

The tempo is so slow as to put a considerable strain on the broad simplicity of the whole, especially in its coda (bb.91–

112). The resulting problem is solved by cultivating a rich singing tone ranging from a Chopinesque lightness in the very rapid semidemiquavers to an Italian *bel canto* in the long notes. Dannreuther, in the second volume of *Musical Ornamentation*, has recorded the almost incredibly slow tempo over which Rubini could sustain Donizetti's or Bellini's melodies.

Bars 1, 3 etc. Four stiff demisemiquavers never make a graceful turn. Think of these turns generally as five notes with the first one tied to the previous long note ⟨music⟩

Then you can vary your interpretation to ⟨music⟩ ⟨music⟩ and ⟨music⟩ This freedom to vary is one reason why ornaments are not written out in full.

bb.17–21 This dramatic gesture is very difficult to execute impressively. The arpeggios are a kind of portamento and should arise as if tied to the top note. The short quaver at the bottom should be very full in tone. In b.21 the situation is different: the arpeggio begins with an accent and is not so quick.

bb.24 ff. Staccato quavers would be an abomination in the accompaniments of this Adagio. Think of chords on a combination of bassoons and horns, the breath sustained and the notes just articulated with the tip of the tongue.

bb.28–30 In even the slowest tempo that can be tolerated these bars will need a little licence if they are not to be a scramble. Keep bb.28 & 30 broad to the end, not merely at the difficult part.

b.31 The licence is needed in the opposite way in this urgent passage, which, however, must not be noticed to exceed the natural swing of the tempo. Remember that quaver chords are big sustained affairs, and that a dotted quaver with a demisemiquaver rest differs only by a slight catch of the breath from a sustained double-dotted quaver.

b.41 Practise the standard six-note trill with three fingers here

If you eventually find it impossible in the time, nothing is easier than to cut off the first note or two. The remainder will prove enormously the better for your practice.

Note also the difference between *rinforzando*, a general increase of tone, and *sforzando*, a local accent.

b.45 Take pedal for exactly one quaver. Begin your arpeggio on the beat, play every note with full tone, and do not *stretch* the chord at all, but carry your hand along it, drawing your fingers up after you like a harpist. Beethoven draws a clear distinction between a continued arpeggio-sign and a separate one for each hand. The continued sign is, however, so often broken in printing by a mark of expression that we may be allowed to conjecture that this has happened here.

Prestissimo

A perversity in the nature of things makes Beethoven use the direction *Prestissimo* in two movements (here and in Op.109), where a warning is needed against playing too fast. But in both cases Beethoven is in a dilemma caused by the fact that the tempo lies on the border-line of two rhythmic standards. A common-time signature here would contradict the unquestionably *alla-breve* character of just the quietest parts of the movement. On the other hand, the semiquavers must be as fast as clearness permits. Beethoven is really thinking of 𝐂 in reference to *Prestissimo*, and of 𝇍 in reference to his accents. Bars 27–37 contain the most difficult passage to play rhythmically. Master this first and do not let the rest of the movement outrun your best playing of these bars.

Bar 1   A fairly strong accent on the E♮ will be needed to make the rhythm clear as having its first accent here and not earlier. The first of the bar will, in fact, need special weight throughout the theme; and the crotchets should be given their full length. These points ought not to be written as marks of expression, for their object is merely to secure that the listener hears what is written in the notes themselves. A border-line case is that of *sostenuto* marks here added to the crotchets. Such marks were not known to Beethoven, who relied on the faint hope that the player would notice the absence of a dot or dash.

bb.14–15   The *sforzandos* belong to the l.h. The right shares in them only to the extent indicated by a staccato dot under the corresponding thumb-notes. This kind of thumb-staccato or finger-staccato is characteristic of Beethoven's early pianoforte style and deserves a better fate than to be bowdlerised away. It survives as late as Op.110.

bb.16–26   The student cannot too early begin to take pleasure in the delicious colour of chords or notes sustained (without pedal) through a finger-staccato in the same hand. The more obvious case in the l.h. should not prevent attention being given to the first half of b.17, and of b.19, in this matter. Pedal may be taken on the first crotchet of b.22, but if it lasts longer than a crotchet the student will lose his opportunity for learning how a melody-note can reverberate by itself. Notice also that in bb.23 and 25 the *fp* is confined to the l.h.

b.31   The reading E♮ as the bass-note of the chord is interesting, but does not bear investigation. The moment for a tonic pedal does not come till bb.43–45.

b.54   On an instrument of wider compass Beethoven would doubtless have carried his climax up to A♭. But we do not know exactly how he would have executed this. The difference would begin at b.53, and we cannot say whether in b.54 he would remain on the A♭ or descend (as in l.h.) to B♮. Nor, in the last resort, can we be very sure that any of the possible alternatives would really be stronger than what he actually wrote.

b.87   The *sforzando* at the end of this bar is a new detail depending on the new accompaniment. Thus it should not be transferred by analogy to b.30, though the *crescendo* is as necessary in bb.28–30 as in 85–87.

b.106   Note the distinction between *calando* (failing or fainting, a matter of tone), and *ritardando*.

bb.113–114   Mark the contrast between the mysterious chord, now at an intense *pianissimo*, held (from the bottom A upwards) by pedal, and the *fortissimo* chord plucked like harp-strings and instantly damped. In the *ritardando* and Adagio see that the rhythm 𝅘𝅥𝅮· 𝅘𝅥𝅮𝅘𝅥 does not become unrecognisable. In such positions the quaver must not be too slow. In b.114 keep the *fortissimo* right into the next bar.

b.121   No pedal! And no *ritardando*! But do not clip the crotchets.

Donald Francis Tovey

Dedicated to the Countess von Browne

SONATA
in C minor

BEETHOVEN, Op.10 No.1

Allegro molto e con brio

(a) Original version, appears later as

Adagio molto

FINALE
Prestissimo

SONATA in F major, Op.10 No.2

Allegro

Like the first movement of Op.14 No.2, and the rondos in Op.7 and 22, this tempo is on a quaver standard such as is commoner in Haydn's early works than in later music, but not unlikely to recur when a style is cultivated at a ripe stage of development. The present tempo is considerably too fast for 4-in-a-bar; yet demisemiquavers are its chief mode of vibration, and semiquavers are purely melodic, needing to break into triplets before they can become mere figures of accompaniment. Take your tempo from bb.9–10.

Bars 1–3 The triplet figure is melody, not a mere twiddle. Even the dot over the crotchet should not reduce that note to a quaver.

b.5 The first semiquaver is dotted in later recurrences. This is a variation, not a discrepancy.

bb.5–8 Get a fine legato in the l.h.

bb.9–10 The 6-note shake and turn  should be easy here. In b.10 put the first grace-note on the beat and do not let it spoil the end of b.9.

bb.31–35 The *sforzandos*, though strongly marked, should not heat this passage up beyond its fundamental *piano*.

bb.38–39 The 4-note turn 𝄢 is best here.

b.42 The *fortissimo* is very characteristic of Beethoven's early marking. He knows as well as we do that there is not much tone to be got from this passage; but in spiritual energy there is not much to choose between kittens and tigers.

bb.46–50 A beautiful example of the difference between dashes and dots. No wonder Beethoven was anxious about it. Here we have positive evidence that these bars are not to be hard or spiky, but in contrast to 44–45.

bb.69–76 A test of steadiness and clearness of rhythm in both hands. Do not spoil the grace of b.72 and the surprise of the sudden *forte* by either the crescendo of stupid virtuosos or the hustle of players who will not practise

patiently. Play b.72, with a 4-note turn 𝄢 as if nothing could disturb it, and meanwhile make a mental image of the exact muscular sensation of a firmly-grasped D minor chord. Then translate that idea into action, not forcing the tone but letting it grow with confidence and experience. Stimulate this by the good *forte* you can easily get in the l.h., and keep this up all through b.76.

b.77 Note that only the outlying bass-notes are staccato. The chords should be *tenute*, like soft horns and bassoons, or strings playing with the *louré* stroke in which the bow moves in one direction, halting but not leaving the strings.

b.202 It is possible that you may have time to play this sonata to please yourself, instead of confining your view of it to that of a concert-player with an overcrowded programme and a mortal fear of those eminent critics whose knowledge of early Beethoven is confined to the statement that 'this smacks of the schoolroom'. Beethoven himself

retained a special affection for this sonata long after he was out of sympathy with most of his early works. If you try the effect, you will discover that he meant something very definite by directing a repeat of the second part. The rise to the dominant of D minor is quite a new point; the whole episodic development, like Mozart's examples of the kind, seems to become more organic by repetition, and the delicious and subtle recapitulation *via* D major gives the more pleasure for the memory that makes it expected. Even with both repeats the movement will not take eight minutes.

Allegretto

Beethoven's early lyric pathos is at its height in this quiet movement. With the exception of Beethoven's long slurs in the l.h. of bb.23–24 and 27–28, which are here corrected to this model in the recapitulation in bb.155–156 & 159–160, the whole is adequately covered by the general advice to make sure that you are playing exactly what Beethoven has written. Do not neglect the normal accentuation of the first beat of each bar when there is no cross-rhythm, and do not obliterate cross-rhythm *sforzandos* by equally strong normal accents. Lastly, do not (in spite of the bad example here given in bb.23–24 & 27–28) level down the differences between first statements and their repetitions. The repeats are written out in full for the express purpose of delicate differences. Find these out for yourself and bring them out in your playing as if you meant them. If in memorising this movement you feel vague about them, you must realise that your work has only just begun, and that technical difficulty is here only a small part of the problem.

Bar 6 The grace-note is probably short, as in the Menuet of Op.2 No.1.

b.15 Note that the bass is D♭, not D♮ as in b.147.

b.42 Turn of three notes before the beat: 𝄢 .

bb.168–169 When you have realised the pathos of the whole, you may feel offended by the *forte* end. Why not *piano*, as in bb.36–37? But when you understand *that*, you will know something worth knowing about Beethoven.

Presto

After two movements that make no demands on an advanced technique, Beethoven gives us a finale as difficult as many later things four times as large. Although the movement is extremely lively, the direction *Presto* should be followed with caution. A lively delivery should be and can be achieved at an obviously safe pace, and this should be taken as the limit until years of experience have given the player a reserve of athletic form sufficient for bigger things. A scrambling performance of this movement is among the ugliest experiences in music, and is permanently hurtful to the technique and style of the scrambler. The scrambler himself would probably have a poor opinion of the final tempo of a great player in this movement. So the young student need not be discouraged: the safe pace may prove fast enough after all.

Bar 1   In Mozart's day it was always assumed that in the absence of marks a solo player would begin a theme *poco forte* or *mezzo piano*. The latter mark (given in brackets) meets the situation here.

b.8   The all-important feature in this bar is the entry of a new voice on the G in r.h. It is hardly possible to make this clear unless l.h. takes over the last semiquaver.

b.23   Let the *piano* be sudden here and at b.125. It is poor playing and poor interpretation to let the tone drop before it, or to begin with a bump.

Learn a good staccato in the left thumb and forefinger over a well-sustained *and rhythmic* little finger:

Strange to say, this is, by the very reason of the fixed little finger, a delightful exercise for loosening the wrist. Bring out the theme in this l.h. passage, also in bb.69–84 and in the recapitulation, keeping r.h. very light.

b.150   The effect of repeating the second part is not a very evident triumph of Beethoven's imagination, the irruption of A♭ (♭III.) being characteristically violent but not quite convincing. But why not try it out and see if it convinces you? The pause applies only to the real end of the sonata, and it should not intervene at the moment of making the repeat.

DONALD FRANCIS TOVEY

Dedicated to the Countess von Browne

SONATA
in F

BEETHOVEN Op. 10 No. 2

SONATA in D major, Op.10 No.3

Presto
Not *prestissimo*. The second minim should be countable.

Bars 1–10 An accent at the beginning of b.2, slightly stronger than the normal accent in the first full bar, will greatly strengthen the sense of rhythm. Analysis shows that there is a slight ambiguity as to which bars are the stronger of their pairs, and the balance of probability is in favour of an accent on b.2.

Do not weaken the *sf* in b.4 by a *crescendo*. There is a finer latent energy in the added octaves, without an increase of loudness.

bb.16–22 Beethoven means exactly what he writes – viz., the broken octaves staccato from the first note; the *crescendo* where he puts it; and, in bb.21–22, three *equal fortissimo* notes, not two strong accents separated by a weaker one. To make this point a slight holding-back is necessary, such as will not attract attention in itself. (A written mark would indicate that the composer wanted for these three notes an emergency-brake effect.)

bb.23–53 This passage ought to need but slight concession (in the first eight bars) to fit into the main tempo. Make it your ambition to draw a grand *cantabile* line over bb.41–45, with that breve (two tied semibreves) and the two following semibreves, before the scale thus begun bursts into a rush of quavers.

bb.53 etc. The grace-note is long, as Czerny rightly pointed out. But he did his best to discredit his evidence by tracing here a derivation from the main theme. Such fancies only injure one's power of seeing real points of structure.

Why does Beethoven write these appoggiaturas as grace-notes? Because a grace-note implies a certain freedom of rhythm. Here we can do with something a little heavier than a quaver, and it need not always be the same size. When the phrase has been announced with a slight rubato, its repetitions may become lighter.

bb.66 ff. Bring out the bass where it alludes to figure (a) of the main theme, but do not neglect the new melody above it.

bb.104–105 Beethoven would obviously have carried his figure up to the top A if his pianoforte had not stopped at F. It is quite legitimate to make the correction here; though when the distortion is not positively unintelligible there is always some interest in the way Beethoven manages it.

b.130 Do not argue from the *crescendo* here that it ought to have been present in b.2. The minor mode needs a new emphasis here.

b.171 Only *forte*, not *ff* here. This gives room for the *crescendo* at 179 and the *ff* at 181.

b.173 A strong accent must here be given by the right thumb to supply the A on which the previous G♯ resolves.

bb.198–199 Only the compass of the pianoforte prevents Beethoven from writing

in b.199, and he might have wished for the top G at the end of b.198 also.

bb.209–210 The new detail of the throbbing inner part adds greatly to the excitement of the recapitulation.

bb.306, 310, 314 A slight accent is desirable on the first note of each of these bars to show the rhythmic periods. The *sforzando* given in many editions on the B♭ in b.316 is a blunder of the uniformitarian editor, acting on a false analogy with b.318. It merely throws the sequel into confusion, for the joint 316–317 is the end of the quiet periods, and the business of the *sforzandos* begins at 317–318. Here there is a rhythmic overlap. The *sforzando* A♭ is twice given as the 7th of the dominant of E♭; then at bb.320–321 it becomes an augmented 6th. Play the E♮ in b.321 with intention, and regard that bar (with the previous crotchet) as the first of a pair, making three such pairs from 321 (inclusive) to the close into 327, which begins a new period. Memorise the whole passage, from 306 (with previous crotchet), as an early item of your work on this sonata. These big and subtle rhythmic expanses are among the central elements in Beethoven's art.

bb.333–340 Bring out the bass augmentation of figure (a) in the finger-staccato characteristic of Beethoven's early pianoforte style.

bb.341–344 Here, as usual, the repeated marks of *ff* and *sf* are meant to override the normal distinction between strong and weak bars or beats. No slackening of rhythm should soften the abruptness of this end. On the other hand, it should not sound hurried – and here the metronome must not override the judgment of an ear that estimates by clearness of detail.

Largo e mesto (*Mesto* = troubled)
The details of phrasing and tone-colour have been provided with extraordinary precision by Beethoven himself; and if you simply make sure that you are playing what is written you will go far to realise the tragic power that makes this movement a landmark in musical history. This is no mechanical task; the student who is capable of holding all the details together in a steady rhythm already shows thereby a feeling for the whole. Do not try to understand *before* you do as Beethoven bids. The people who 'understand' great music beforehand will never see anything in it except a mirror of their own minds. The player who obeys orders faithfully will be constantly discovering their real meaning.

This warning must suffice; there is no other practical advice than to repeat, bar after bar, that Beethoven means exactly what he has written. A conspicuous instance, disguised in many editions by bad printing, is to be found in bb.23–24 & 62–63, where the sustained dotted crotchets reverberate through the *piano* semiquavers with an effect that no pedal could produce.

The tempo is broad enough for b.10, but flowing enough for the episodic figure of bb.36–43. In this passage do not allow the pedal to retain the grace-notes, though these should come on the beat, not before it. (There is no difficulty in this – the *fp* will be accepted by the ear as a main beat though it arrives late – but if the grace-notes have come before the metronome-beat, they will have clipped the previous beat unpleasantly.)

In bb.41–43 it is not enough to count six; you must imagine a steady flow of demisemiquavers as a framework for the whole.

Bars 68–71 Do not let the arpeggios become weak or sticky, but carry your hand over them and gather up your fingers like a harpist.

bb.75–76 Go straight to the end of this scale; nothing can be duller than a *ritardando* here. On the other hand, of course, do not clip it; and listen to the octave D throughout its two full beats.

Menuetto

The deep poetry of this movement must be conveyed in Beethoven's *allegro* tempo, without even so much concession to sentimental playing as *allegretto*. The tempo should, in fact, be given by the ostentatiously prosaic trio with its energetic triplets; and with no slackness in bb.67–70. Much practice will be needed before adequate expression can be given to the minuet at that pace; and accuracy and tone-management should first be attained slower. The danger then will be that you may fall in love with the slower tempo and miss the truth of the beauty.

At the beginning, see that the inner part of the r.h. does not interfere with the melody. This minuet is a favourite melody of many inexpert listeners; and when they hum

it as  etc.

they betray a sad state of things.

The *sforzandos* in bb.17, 19, 21 & 23 do not make a *forte*. If you have not a good shake with your outside fingers, b.25 is an opportunity for learning one. The 'false trill' will not do here. On the other hand, you need not be able to stretch a 10th in order to take the melody of this bar with the l.h., for a pedal through the bar is quite safe.

At b.31 the *ff* in the bass is a more violent mark than Beethoven would have used in later works. Yet he would probably consider it justified if he could hear how we tend to smooth him down.

The last fourteen bars are a touchstone for delicacy and truthfulness of playing. Express the difference between B♭ and B♮ as if you quite simply mean it – neither as if you wished to protest it, nor as if you had not noticed it.

Rondo: Allegro

A comfortable 4 in the bar is quite fast enough for this very witty and difficult movement. Get a clear accent on the true first beat (the G) and take no liberty with the time except immediately before the pause in b.4.

Bar 33 The *f* or *ff* given in most editions is possibly right, though it may have been an officious guess prompted by the thick chord and the abrupt change. In any case the *sforzandos* will soon produce a *forte*, and the following episode is clearly in a violent temper.

bb.34/35–40 Beethoven has marked only the first two notes (A, B♭) as thematic; but the allusion is almost certainly intentional throughout the passage. Do not bring

it out by holding the notes down, but simply let the bass rattle in a clear finger-staccato unclouded by pedal. The

design  etc.

will then express itself unobtrusively, and the Beethovenish overlappings of harmony at bb.36, 38 & 40 will have their effect.

b.48 Note that the last quaver is outside the pause, and do not pause too long.

bb.84–86 Look after the normal accents here, especially the third beat of b.85, which is liable to get obscured.

bb.92–99 Note Beethoven's characteristic finger-staccato in l.h. at the *sforzandos*. Do not fail to express the change of step in them at b.96. At b.98 the first grace-note obviously emerges slowly, as if from a tied D:

b.110 In some early editions a very silly person inserted a *crescendo* leading to a *fortissimo* end. If people still exist who do not see the point of a *pianissimo* arpeggio without pedal and with an exact final crotchet, why consider their interests?

At b.108 it would surely be legitimate to read as follows:

DONALD FRANCIS TOVEY

Dedicated to the Countess von Browne

SONATA
in D major

BEETHOVEN, Op.10 No.3

MENUETTO
Allegro

TRIO

Menuetto D.C. ma senza replica

RONDO
Allegro

SONATA in C minor, Op.13

(*SONATA PATHÉTIQUE*)

Apart from the first movement, this sonata is not technically very difficult; but the first movement needs the staying-power required for big things. Its difficulty is of a kind that can be and ought to be mastered by young players if it is to be mastered at all. The danger is that young players are apt to attack it without any idea of the steady and cautious work that it needs. The student's first ambition should be to acquire a good tremolo. The l.h. of bb.1–17 of the *Allegro di molto e con brio*, and all quaver vibrations in either hand, will need long and habitual practice with a loose wrist and carefully graduated *crescendos* at a very moderate and steady pace, always with the exact number of notes as written. Patience in this matter will be as surely rewarded as premature forcing of pace and tone will lead to chronic discouragement and a lowering of the player's standards. Before attempting anything else, then, learn what it feels like and sounds like to get a really continuous vibration (not necessarily very fast) in bb.1–17 of the *Allegro di molto*, with a fine steady *crescendo* in bb.5–8 & 13–16, right up to the drop back to *piano*.

Grave

Keep semiquavers in mind as the rhythmic background throughout, realising that a demisemiquaver, such as that of the rising octave from b.1 to b.2, is no mere click but a good vocal note. The tempo should not be so slow that the nine semidemisemiquavers in the last semiquaver of b.4 can fit in without some slight concession; but the concession should not attract attention.

Before playing anything else, try bb.9–10, counting sixteen semiquavers and taking a tempo that will easily get eight notes of the penultimate chromatic scale into each. This tempo will, as already suggested, be a little too slow; but so long as you feel any doubt as to the length of the rests and the position of each of the sixteen semiquaver beats, you must be content to play by machinery. Obey orders first, and understand the result by its effect.

Allegro di molto e con brio

Bars 1–16 The tempo must not be too fast for the rhythm and harmony of b.3, though the tremolo in the bass must be a good steady vibration of exact quavers. Beethoven does not give sforzandos in bb.3 & 11. Editors have supplied them on the analogy of bb.187 & 195; but Beethoven probably meant this as a variation. Of course, the syncopation will of itself produce a slight accent if clearly expressed.

bb.41–78 If you find that you cannot play this as fast as the opening, then you should regard your opening tempo as too fast – at all events for your present powers. Remember that it is very unimportant whether you take six months or six years in screwing this Allegro up until you can break speed-records, but that it is very important for your own harmonious development that you should not play it badly at any stage of your practice. At b.41 the semibreves of the l.h. obviously continue the connecting link of bb.39–40. Get the two-part dialogue of r.h. steadily rhythmic, and do not put up with banal quaver triplets for

the *Pralltriller* in bb.47–48 etc. Take three fingers to them, thus:

bb.83–102 Notice Beethoven's dashes and the purposeful distinction between them and the dots in bb.89–90 & 101–102. Of course, dots and dashes here alike mean a finger-staccato, not a lifting of the whole hand. Beethoven was, at this period and later, very urgent that 'the distinction between dots and dashes is not a matter of indifference'. But he failed, no less than his printers and editors, to achieve consistency in this matter – so much so that his intentions are seldom as intelligible as in this Exposition. And, if Mandyczewski has committed no oversight, the Recapitulation of this very movement throws the matter into confusion again! This has been remedied in the present edition.

b.122 Presumably the repeat is from the beginning of the Allegro, though Beethoven gives no evidence that it is not (as in the Quartet, Op.130) to include the Grave! This is, however, unlikely: the whole Grave is obviously too long for the purpose. Not much is lost, and something is gained, by omitting the repeat altogether.

bb.129–138 The complete transformation of the figure of the Grave in these bars shows the futility of the modern idea that the contrasted tempi ought to stand in some exact aliquot ratio.

bb.138–152 Beethoven gives no indication that this *crescendo* is not to last until the sudden *piano* at b.153. There is, however, unusual difficulty in maintaining this; and there is nothing impossible in supposing that a *diminuendo* has been accidentally omitted at b.149.

bb.157–160 Express these beautiful harmonies by a *legatissimo* r.h. without pedal and in contrast to a very dry and light tremolo in the bass.

bb.201, 205 The sudden *piano* must be expressed both times, but it will need caution or the chord will vanish altogether. Aim at a solemn clear tone.

b.285 The previous chord must cease with an abruptness that makes a rhythmic event of the silence at the beginning of this bar. It is as important to count sixteen here as in the original introduction.

Adagio Cantabile

Take your tempo from a quite broad delivery of b.22, and rely on your singing tone to maintain interest without impatience. The triplets in b.8 are a touchstone for your sense of rhythm. Treat them as if a new voice had entered on C.

Bar 21 The turn should come *after* the dot.

not, as usual, on it.

b.48 The bracketed *sempre piano* is necessitated by the fact that Czerny, here and in the next bar, inserted a *rinforzando* which has gained wide currency. Seldom has interference been more disastrous! Until I became aware that this mark was spurious, I always thought that bb.47–50 comprised the last examples of a certain lack of breadth that marks the transitions in some of Beethoven's earliest works. But Beethoven did nothing to isolate these bars. They should be absolutely continuous with the previous theme, into the course of which they introduce a dark harmonic cloud which, in the authentic *crescendo* of b.50, leads to the home tonic. In other words, these three bars are an expansion of a four-bar phrase (from b.45) to six bars, not a truncated and perfunctory new passage.

Rondo: *Allegro*

The pathos of this movement is modified by a humour that puts a considerable strain on the title *Pathétique* which Beethoven's publisher forced upon the whole sonata.

Some editions have **C**, others **₵** as the time-signature. The proper tempo is distinctly beyond the bounds of **C**, but is obviously a very different **₵** from that of the first movement. The triplet quavers of bb.33–41 must not be scrambled, and the main theme, up to b.17, must neither drag as a whole nor pinch its grace-notes in bb.5–6. These must on no account be taken before their beat. Bar 41, with its last pair of quavers after the triplets, is a touchstone of rhythm.

Bars 9–10 etc.   We may well despair of the distinction between dots and dashes when we find that the original editions give dashes in these melodic passages. In the present edition dashes are used only where *cantabile* style is not in question.

bb.35–43   Beethoven leaves this unmarked. All we know is that the tone probably rises some way beyond the new *piano* at b.44.

bb.59, 118 & 200   Note the care with which Beethoven avoids the stiffness of eight equal semiquavers and concordant notes on the beats at the end of the run. His accelerated scales must always be practised in the exact rhythm he prescribes; the result at full speed is no bizarre accentuation, but real brilliance and continuity.

b.78   Do not be perfunctory with the important leading quavers in this bar. All such introductory notes should enter with a clear gesture. Treat the whole episode as thoroughly *cantabile* in all voices, and mark the entry of a new idea at the join 94–95 just as much as if that idea were going to be developed at leisure instead of hardly lasting four bars.

bb.107–112   This passage needs firm fingers, pulled up harpwise after each note; no pedal; and a dramatic quality like the crescendo of side-drums. Pedal should enter at b.117, and it may then be safely continued halfway down the scale. A *piano* is necessary at 107 to make room for the *crescendo*.

b.128   The *cantabile* of the l.h. begins with this bar. Some early editors marked this passage *agitato*. They showed thereby more agitation than discretion, though they were right in being moved.

bb.136–137   The bracketed rest and part-director indicates the probability that the middle notes in bb.135–136 are not a mere filling out but an early entry of the middle voice.

b.140   There is no indication how long this *crescendo* is to last. A sudden *piano* at 143 is highly probable. After-

wards another increase of tone is implied, as in bb.36–43.

bb.186–188   These bars continue the preceding *ff* as far as their two-part texture permits. Bar 189 then enters with a dramatic sudden *piano*.

bb.202/203–210   It is a structural as well as a sentimental mistake to slacken the tempo here. The theme is pretending to start a new development in a new key, and the whole point here is that it nevertheless ends the whole work within a normal eight-bar phrase. Early editions mark the last bar *fff*, a mark which, though used by Beethoven on a very few sublime occasions, here suggests the agitated editor who could not control his feelings in bb.128–131.

DONALD FRANCIS TOVEY

Dedicated to Prince Carl von Lichnowsky

SONATA
in C minor

(SONATA PATHÉTIQUE)

BEETHOVEN, Op.13

Attacca subito il' Allegro

Allegro di molto e con brio

(L.H.under)

Adagio cantabile

RONDO
Allegro

SONATA in E major, Op.14 No.1

Beethoven's wonderful arrangement of this sonata as a string quartet should be in the hands of every student. It is published in miniature score (No.297 of the Payne-Eulenburg series) with the original sonata interlined. Unfortunately, the original sonata has been printed from an instructive edition which conventionalises Beethoven's marks in the usual instructive-destructive style, and thereby sheds grave suspicion on the marking for strings, besides making it difficult to compare this with the true pianoforte marking. The string marks, however, seem authentic as far as one can judge them on their merits. Further remarks on this quartet version will be found in *A Companion to Beethoven's Sonatas*.* A good rehearsal of it by competent players is a lesson in style such as no other piece of music can give. Quartet players are apt to miss the point, and to see only the obvious fact that neither as music nor as quartet-writing can this by no means easy opusculum compare with Beethoven's original quartets. Of course it cannot; if it could, the pianoforte sonata would have been superseded by translation into the more perfect medium, and Beethoven, instead of purposely choosing one of his smallest works for this translation, would never have troubled to write for the pianoforte again. We have here a unique demonstration of what the pianoforte can do better than strings, what qualities of bowed instruments it can really imitate, what qualities it can suggest without imitating, and in what characteristics it is, as Beethoven said in a letter to his publisher, totally opposite to the string quartet. There are not eight consecutive bars of this string-version without some detail which sheds new light on the meaning of Beethoven's pianoforte style.

Allegro

There is a temptation to take this movement far too fast. It is really in rather a reflective mood, all the more clearly shown by the apparent inconsequence of the first paragraph with its four disconnected but self-repeating ideas crowded into twelve bars. Take a tempo in which, after patient slow practice, it is not impossible to deliver the infuriatingly treacherous bb.5–6 without symptoms of intoxication, and with a definite purpose in playing A♯ at the end of b.6. Contrive in bb.10–11 to make the long melody note ♩♪· sing without failing before it descends the scale.

In bb.1–4 observe Beethoven's phrasing, and take care that the octaves on the half-bars are lighter and not heavier than the main beats.

The turn in b.8 is of four notes, not five. Grace-notes like those of the l.h. arpeggio  are better than absorbing the whole quaver into a group of four demisemiquavers. The pedal must not retain the bass arpeggio.

Bars 16–20 The quartet version treats the melody as a 2-bar phrase, the repetitions a third higher being in an imitating voice.

b.17 Unlike the next sonata (Op.14 No.2), this work is full of big stretches. Small hands should break the quaver rhythm in the *piano* stretches ♩♩♩♪ ₇ ♩♩♪ and should arpeggiate the *forte* ones, taking care to put the bass-note on the beat.

b.31 It is not an oversight that the melody is here legato instead of in the mezzo-staccato of bb.23–30.

b.59 Take the C♯ (or both C♯ and B) in l.h.

bb.155, 158, 159, 160 Small hands may play alternately

 and ⟨notation⟩ in the second halves of these bars.

Allegretto

In this wonderful movement the soft full chords of the pianoforte are far more beautiful than the line-drawing of the string-quartet, which is here starved for want of material. The student can learn a priceless lesson from the severity with which Beethoven confines the strings to the fewest possible notes, relying on their pure individual tone and unencumbered phrasing, though almost every note of the pianoforte chords could have been reached by double stops.

Strange to say, the portamento in b.62, which anybody would guess to be a purely 'violinistic' idiom, suits the pianoforte far better than the violin. With pedal and a *gentle* accent at the top, the pianoforte can suggest it; and there is nothing to contradict the suggestion. The violin cannot suggest it: we do not accept suggestions when we know that the instrument can do the real thing. But this real thing lies awkwardly across three strings.

The only advice the student needs will be found to come to the sempiternal exhortation to trust Beethoven and play what he writes. Separate bb.1, 2 according to his slurs; take the crescendo as leading to the *sf* but not further; and treat the *sf* as initiating a slightly fuller tone in the sequel, until *p* is resumed.

Some editions read D♯ instead of F♯ at the end of b.50; but the evidence, including that of the string-quartet, is in favour of F♯. But we must not use the string-quartet as evidence when Beethoven is altering the scoring. It gives no excuse for altering b.60, where at least two other readings have been proposed.

Bar 100 Obviously 'sin' al Maggiore' means 'up to (but not including) the Maggiore'. On the *da capo* the portamento of b.62 closes into the Coda.

Rondo: *Allegro commodo*

Commodo means 'at a convenient pace', or 'as fast as is comfortable'. Consequently, the ambitious player is apt to make it a point of honour to play as fast as is uncomfortable. In a really convenient tempo the semiquaver scale-figure in this movement is (like bb.5–6 in the first movement) a witticism in the theme, not an impediment of speech comical only to the unfeeling spectator. But the tempo is definitely an *alla breve*, and is, in fact, almost exactly that of the Rondo of Op.13.

* *A Companion to Beethoven's Pianoforte Sonatas: A Complete Book of Analyses*. (Associated Board)

The first thing to master is the l.h. of the first phrase. In this kind of passage impatience is ruinous to your technique. As an alternative method of practice, try it in legato unbroken chords; not squirming painfully with complicated fingerings, but moving quietly along the whole series of positions:

The next thing is to realise and make quite purposeful the sudden *piano* at the beginning of b.4. A really brutal philistinism inflicted a *forte* here in some quite early and many modern editions. Some excuse may be found for this in the fact that the string-version reads *forte*, though none of the editors who would impose it on the pianoforte version had ever heard of this. But the conditions of the string-scoring are altogether different: the sudden *piano* implies an instrument of percussion; and Beethoven gives the strings a totally different accompaniment, and a new rhythmic figure at b.4.

Let us at once memorise this sudden *piano* as an essential feature of the pianoforte theme, and let us see where and why it is twice replaced by a *forte*. First, then, it becomes *forte* at b.42, when the theme has decided to plunge into a remote key; secondly, it makes a *crescendo* leading to a *fortissimo* at b.112, when, near the end of the movement, the theme is varied by syncopation. (As a matter of fact, this syncopation suggested to Beethoven the scheme of scoring of the theme throughout the movement in the quartet version.) To these cases we must add the absence of any crescendo at 'all in the final *pp* chromatic variation, bb.121–125.

In the G major episode (bb.47 f.) note Beethoven's finger-staccato. Do not load this with clouds of pedal. Reserve your pedal for bb.58–65 and bb.76–79. A little judicious pedal is good at moments in the chromatic scale, especially in the *decrescendo*, where even a little blurring may be acceptable. These things are harmful only when the player is not aware that he is doing them, or, being aware, does not listen to their effect.

Some editors like an echo effect at bb.76–79, giving 76–77 *forte* and 78–79 *piano*. Beethoven is not fond of such effects, and can indicate them when he wants them.

Donald Francis Tovey

Dedicated to the Baroness von Braun

SONATA
in E

BEETHOVEN, Op.14 No.1

Allegretto

Maggiore

Allegretto da capo
sin' al Maggiore,
e poi la Coda.

Coda

RONDO
Allegro commodo

SONATA in G major, Op.14 No.2

Unlike Op.14 No.1, this exquisite little work presents few difficulties to small hands. It is not so easy as the sonatas in Op.49, but it can be studied to advantage by anyone who can master those; and it needs no apology on the score of immaturity. Good work has been done on it even by players whose hands have not yet grown large enough to play b.91 of the first movement comfortably; and it is worthwhile considering their special difficulties.

Allegro

The tempo is of a kind commoner in the early works of Haydn than in later music. A certain ornateness of style prompts the composer to use quavers rather than crotchets as his standard rhythm. The expression is *allegro*, and if the movement were rewritten in *alla breve* time it would look normal enough, the tempo being then just a little too fast for counting four crotchets. Bars 119–120 should not be a scramble.

Bars 19, 41 etc. Never spoil Beethoven's sudden drops to *piano* by ceasing your *crescendo* before them, nor his sudden *fortes* by showing excitement too soon.

b.43 Play D E F♯ E in the second group. The limitation of the pianoforte to the three-spaced F♮ was a mere nuisance to Beethoven here.

b.47 Do not hold down the melody-notes in b.47: Beethoven's deliberate intention is to let the melody assert itself first in the next bar.

At b.49 a judicious pedal on the third quaver will relieve small hands of the stretch of a 9th. Or the l.h. may take over the lower semiquavers.

bb.81–96 This is the hardest passage in the sonata, except the themes of the Scherzo. The staccatos in the bass give the young player a splendid opportunity of laying a firm foundation for this part of his technique. The positions of the whole l.h. passage should be first learnt in legato and then practised in a heavy staccato. Mark the normal accented beats throughout: this is the first protection against unevenness of tone. It is a mistake to regard this passage as presenting difficulty in playing triplets against pairs. That difficulty exists only at a slow pace; and while you are still under the necessity of practising the l.h. slowly you have no business to play both hands together at all. Divide the passage into sections according to its natural phrasing and master each group in turn. Then see if you can play the whole without fatigue. Last of all, add the r.h.

For very small hands the arpeggio of b.91 is troublesome. To alter it alone would lead to bad grammar. Here is a grammatically correct way out of the difficulty, beginning at b.90.

b.97 is troublesome for any but a full-grown l.h. Small hands must master the following device:

b.102 With an instrument of larger compass, Beethoven would have made this bar rise to A♭, corresponding with b.4. But the necessity of this is not as strong as many editors seem to think. Within another two bars the passage entirely ceases to be parallel to the opening, and it may just as well diverge at b.102 as later.

b.124 Connect the C♯ in your mind, with the *upper* D, and do not make an hiatus after the pause.

Andante

With experienced players there is a natural tendency to take this ironically simple movement too fast; and the tendency has been given great impetus by the fact that from an early period the time-signature has been printed as *alla breve*. This is not so impossible as it seems in a slow movement: it would not mean counting two minims in a bar, but a mere precaution against playing too slow. In this sense Haydn expressly writes *Largo alla breve* in a very early quartet, Op.2 No.5. The proper tempo for this movement is fixed by the third variation, where the semiquavers must neither be so deliberate that the arpeggios will not coalesce and give a good outline of the theme nor so quick that the scales become runs.

In the first variation (bb.21–40) be careful to bring the theme out in the middle voice, when its notes are in the r.h. as well as when they are in the l.h. If, for instance, you make the listener think that the top part of b.24 is this

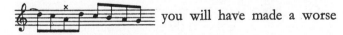 you will have made a worse

blunder than any obvious wrong note.

The syncopated counterpoint in the r.h. should deliver its repeated notes like a nightingale, not like a hen.

In the second variation (bb.41–60) the bass on the beats may be as staccato as you please, but the syncopated chords (including their l.h. notes) should be rich, like soft wood-wind without oboes. The *sf* crotchets in bb.46–48 and the three *forte* quavers in b.58 should not be staccato at all. The semiquavers at the ends of bb.44 & 48 should be thought of as leading in each case to the next accent in spite of the apparent hiatus.

Bars 61–64 This short interlude cannot be too wistful, though the tempo should not drag.

b.65 The *piano* is evidently implied by the rest of the variation, and it should be a clear contrast to the previous

pp. There is no such rhythmic figure as ♪♫ here; nor is this variation a duet between the two hands, except at the places where Beethoven takes advantage of that possibility. But the initial idea is that of smooth arpeggios arising from the bass and outlining the melody, together with inner parts that come and go or are varied by passing notes (such as the F♯ in b.65) as need arises. In short, the scheme is this –

with a sustained bass that sometimes becomes independent.

b.90   Do not be ladylike over this last chord. It is essentially Haydn's Surprise 'at which all the ladies will scream'. On the other hand, do not be satisfied with a wooden bang. Practise a fine, full-toned, full-length crotchet.

Scherzo: *Allegro assai*
Cling to the proper meaning of *assai*. Not 'extremely' but *assez*: lively *enough*. This movement is often attacked at a tempo which would make bb.197–200 a scramble even for experienced players. Make no such mistake. Regard the movement as on the quaver standard, like the first movement; and take it no faster than a comfortable waltz, such as could be danced gracefully if we knew how to waltz nowadays.

Bars 1–22   The paramount necessity for this group of themes is a clear accent on the first of each bar. Few but the most experienced players have any idea how strong an accent is needed before the listener can guess the rhythm at all. The player must make a constant and conscious effect to maintain it against the cross-rhythm; otherwise even the cross-rhythm will vanish for lack of something to cross. Conversely, you must not accentuate any other beats but the first in each bar. If the tempo is not too fast you will have time enough for the proper quizzical expression of the C♯ in b.2, though this is not allowed to have a *sforzando* until near the end of the sonata (bb.239 f.).

These cautions cover most of the movement. Trust Beethoven for the rest; and take even the short slurs in bb.209–212 & 233–236 literally, separating each triplet by a lift of the hand.

Note that at b.237 the theme is delayed by a bar, so that it lies a bar later along its periods. Hence the blank portion of a silent final bar, the main accents falling on bb.249, 251 & 253.

DONALD FRANCIS TOVEY

Dedicated to the Buroness von Braun

SONATA
in G

BEETHOVEN, Op. 14 No. 2

Andante
La prima parte senza replica

SCHERZO
Allegro assai

SONATA in B flat major, Op.22

For its size, its brilliance, and its maturity this work presents surprisingly few difficulties of technique and interpretation. Bar 3 in the first movement is more difficult than anything else in the sonata, and requires the same free forearm and the same method of testing by shifted accents

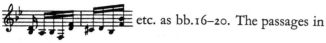 etc. as bb.16–20. The passages in

broken octaves also need the same freedom of muscle; but when they move in scales, it is as well to get a legato in the outside fingers. Bars 44–45 are obviously a good exercise for trills with the little finger.

Perhaps the only serious textual problem is that of the *piano* given by most authorities at b.101. Either this is a mere accidental intrusion or it stands for a stage in some *diminuendo* that has not been indicated – perhaps a *mf* or *mp* – at all events something that leaves room for the sudden *decrescendo* in b.104 and the *p* in b.105. But I am inclined to think that in b.101 the *p* is a mere accident. The suddenness of the *decrescendo* in b.104, reaching a *p* in three crotchets, reads like a dramatic stroke that must not be forestalled, and I believe that Beethoven intended the whole previous thirteen bars to be in full tone.

In bb.30–35 & 38–43 – also 161–166 & 169 – we may take it that the *sforzandos* rest on a background of *mezzo-forte*. A *piano* thus becomes necessary at b.44 (175) as a starting-point for the *crescendo*.

For the rest the student should consult the analysis in *A Companion to Beethoven's Pianoforte Sonatas,** and should trust Beethoven, who was particularly pleased with the smoothness and finish of this work. *Die Sonate hat sich gewaschen*: 'this sonata is in apple-pie order', down to the distinction between dots and dashes, which is here perfectly clear and consistent.

Adagio con molta espressione

All Beethoven's movements in $\frac{9}{8}$ time will be taken too slow if we do not take our time from the dotted crotchets rather than from the quavers. Indeed, Beethoven's first $\frac{9}{8}$ movement, the adagio of the G major string-trio, Op.9 No.1, shows this, for he writes it, at great inconvenience, in $\frac{3}{4}$ time, marking the quavers as triplets. On the other hand, the three main beats will, of course, be very slow indeed. But we must be able to grasp them; and it will not be amiss to pay some attention to marking the accent on the first of each of these huge bars.

Bar 3 Begin the turn well after the second quaver, and then deliver it broadly.

bb.8, 10, 13 The shakes should begin on the upper note.

b.20 A turn in this position is equivalent to [notation] – i.e., [notation] the grace-notes coming before the beat.

bb.30, 77 The grace-notes come on the beat together with the bass. But the inner A in the r.h. may arrive with the melody-note.

b.39 The semiquavers of the r.h. are, of course, in the same voice throughout, and it is a new upper part that enters above them.

Menuetto

Having given this movement its proper title, Beethoven had no need to mark the tempo. If you really want to know how it should be marked, the answer is *Tempo di Menuetto*. As such, it has a good deal of swing, not unlike the glorious minuet in the Septet. But you will lose the swing if you hurry. Note that Beethoven does not wish you to underline the obvious in bb.28–30, but desires the tapering cross-rhythms to run out in an unbroken legato.

Beethoven omits the title of *Trio*, probably accidentally, as he retains the convention of repeating the time-signature.

Bars 31 ff. The *sforzando* cross-accents in r.h. and the general style indicate energy; but there is no conclusive reason that Beethoven intends a *forte*: and perhaps the *sforzandos* produce greater energy on a basis of *mf*.

Rondo: *Allegretto*

This movement is on the quaver standard, a comfortable 4 in the bar, and hardly faster than the *Poco allegretto* of Op.7.

The text is in perfect order to the last dot and dash. Many editors wish to use the upper octave of our pianofortes so as to make bb.34–35 repeat 32–33 an octave higher. They point to bb.147–148, which repeat 145–146 exactly. But the compass of Beethoven's instrument prevented him from going an octave higher there. We may just as well argue that exact repetition was forced on him there as that distortion was forced on him in bb.34–35. The distortion is quite an acceptable variation; and the discrepancy is not worth correcting – especially as there are several ways of correcting it, and all involve some kink in the context.

For one reason and another, all the shakes in this movement will begin on the main note. Those in bb.42–43 will

consist of five notes, including the turn . In b.21

and similar passages the turns over repeated notes follow the rule of b.20 of the Adagio.

It would be a healthy early ambition of the young player to achieve a straightforward performance of this sonata that brought out its beauty by sheer accuracy, together with a due pleasure in the production of good pianoforte tone. The pride of fashion has dictated a persistent under-valuing of this work – as if Beethoven had written himself down by achieving perfection without any show of force or humour. When this despising of normal beauty penetrates into the schoolroom, it hinders the progress of young people who may develop into something much more valuable than the transmitters of fashions. Only a very great composer could have written this sonata, and a good performance of it promises a capacity for presenting the greater things that followed it.

DONALD FRANCIS TOVEY

* *A Companion to Beethoven's Pianoforte Sonatas: A Complete Book of Analyses.* (Associated Board)

Dedicated to the Count von Browne

SONATA
in B flat

BEETHOVEN, Op. 22

Allegro con brio

(a) or

234

Adagio con molta espressione

MENUETTO

Minore [TRIO]

Menuetto Da Capo senza replica

RONDO
Allegretto

Printed in Great Britain by Dotesios Ltd, Trowbridge, Wiltshire.